D1095523

THE CHRONICLES OF

EVOLUTION

SYDNEY BRENNER'S 10-ON-10

THE CHRONICLES OF

EVOLUTION

EDITED BY Shuzhen Sim and Benjamin Seet

WILDTYPE BOOKS

CONTENTS

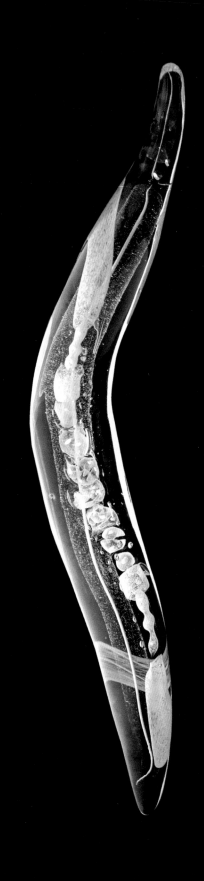

FOREWORD

Sydney Brenner

The study of evolution is a great intellectual challenge for science because it allows us to reconstruct the past and to understand how life began and evolved from simple to complex organisms.

People have always asked whether evolution is constantly driving onwards and upwards. Is there always going to be improvement? The answer is no: evolution is a progression of form and function, but it is not purposeful.

The important lesson to learn here is that only mathematics is the art of the perfect. Physics is the art of the optimal, but biology is the art of the satisfactory: if it works, you keep it; if it doesn't, you get rid of it.

So I think it is very important that we drive out all thoughts of perfect animals or perfect plants. Organisms are merely satisfactory—they work. Some of them don't even work very efficiently, but they work well enough to survive and propagate.

OUR JUNKYARD GENOME

Now, it so happens that we have very recently gained the most remarkable access to the materials of evolution through our ability to sequence DNA. This lets us read the messages written in the genomes of many different bacteria, plants and animals.

It turns out that only one or two percent of the human genome codes for proteins; most of the rest appears to be unnecessary. It is, if you like, rubbish.

OPPOSITE
Glass model of *Caenorhabditis elegans* by Luke Jerram, commissioned for the Sydney Brenner Scientific Symposium held in Singapore in 2015.

I long ago discovered that there are two kinds of rubbish: the kind you keep, which is called junk; and the kind you throw away, which is called garbage.

In 1958 when I was working at Cambridge University, we bought an ultracentrifuge which arrived from California in a beautiful wooden box. I thought I would use the box to make a bookcase, but I never found the time to do it. It was stored in our attic at home for 12 years.

One day I came home and found that my wife had thrown the box away; she said that she knew I would never find the time to make a bookcase and she needed the space for something else. I realised that wives are the agents of natural selection, and mine had converted junk into garbage.

We have to accept that 98 percent of our genome is junk—just something we carry around with us. Not all organisms have as much junk. The pufferfish or *fugu*, for example, has a genome about eight times smaller than ours, but with a similar number of genes. But when people are confronted with this information, they find it paradoxical, because they think that everything is there for a purpose.

......

THE CLOCK IN OUR GENES

When we read genomes, we also notice something else. DNA is composed of the nucleotide bases A, T, C and G. Each of the 20 amino acids—the building blocks of proteins—is specified by a triplet of bases, also known as a codon. But certain amino acids can be represented by more than one codon: for example, GGT, GGC, GGA and GGG all encode the amino acid glycine.

This turns out to be very powerful because in these cases, it doesn't matter which base is present in the third position of the codon. You can make exactly the same organism whether or not there is a mutation there. What this gives us is an internal clock, embedded in the genomes of all organisms, from bacteria all the way up to humans.

If you line up DNA sequences from two organisms, it stands to reason that the greater the number of differences between them, the more distantly related they are. By looking at genomes, you can measure the passage of time, and hence give a description of the whole of evolution, as generation succeeds generation and as the genes of the progeny replace those of their parents.

Using this clock, we very quickly discovered that many organisms evolve so slowly that they appear to be at equilibrium. The coelacanth and the elephant shark, for example, have remained essentially unchanged over hundreds of millions of years. Some bacteria that live in incredible places—for instance, in the boiling water that comes out of vents at the floor of the ocean—have probably been around since the dawn of life, and are very likely exactly the same as they were billions of years ago when life began.

FROM THE EVOLUTIONARY PAST TO THE FUTURE

So we have to be careful—evolution does not always move onwards and upwards. Organisms could just mark the passage of time by this process of mutation, and not change at all.

Other organisms, however, do go through enormous changes. Here, the most important driving force comes from the ability to get extra copies of genes and to change them by mutation. Bacteria, for example, can expand their genomes by taking in DNA from other organisms and assimilating it into their own DNA.

On Earth, we have some understanding of the full course of evolution, going from the beginning of the solar system, to the creation of primitive living cells, to more complex plants and animals, and finally to ourselves and the human systems we have created.

Of course, the most interesting stage of evolution is when we give up doing it by biology. For humans, this is something we already do through our daily experiences, where we bring about change through science, technology, language and culture.

The advent of humans is comparatively recent, perhaps two million years ago. Modern biology only began in 1953, and we still do not understand how our brains work. Science has created many new technologies, and our efforts are likely to exhaust natural resources and change much of the world as we know it.

The future is full of new questions. Will genetic engineering allow us to create new sources of food, and will we be able to create new minds in computers? These are new elements in a complex world, and they will bring about new changes.

INTRODUCTION

In 1954, James Watson and George Gamow founded the RNA Tie Club, a 'gentleman's club' of illustrious scientists who wanted to solve the puzzle of how the genetic code built proteins. As one of the Club's 20 members (one for each amino acid), Sydney Brenner received a necktie and a unique amino acid designation—valine.

Despite its whimsy, the RNA Tie Club became a platform for creative ideas and intellectual discussion about the workings of the genetic code. A number of its members, Sydney included, went on to make seminal contributions to the field of molecular biology.

More than 60 years later, Sydney conceived the idea of an Evolution Club. In the spirit of the RNA Tie Club, the Evolution Club would establish a community of scientists and scholars in Singapore and beyond to discuss evolution in all its variety and complexity. It would also explore ideas on how we got from the Big Bang to where we are today, and where we might end up in the future.

At exactly 10 minutes past the 10th hour on 10 December 2016, the Evolution Club was formed, sans ties and with a lady member. Its five inaugural members were Sydney Brenner, Jan Vasbinder, Balázs Gulyás, Asyifah Rashid and myself.

The central idea was for the Evolution Club to present a series of 10 seminars over 10 months on events spanning 10 billion years. These would follow a logarithmic time scale, beginning 10^{10} years ago with the origin of the universe, then moving on to the origin of biological life 10^9 years ago, and so on, up to the development of modern human society in the present time, or 10^1 years.

In 2017, we invited renowned experts to Singapore to speak on each of these evolutionary milestones. The result was *10-on-10: The Chronicles of Evolution*, a year-long lecture series organised by Nanyang Technological University's Para Limes Society and the Singapore Agency for Science, Technology and Research's (A✳STAR) Biomedical Research Council.

OPPOSITE
In the 1990s, Sydney Brenner led an initiative to sequence the genome of the *Takifugu* pufferfish, also known as *fugu*. Humans and *fugu* share similar repertoires of genes, but the fish's genome has almost no junk DNA.

The first lecture was delivered by Sydney on 21 February 2017. With typical Sydney sagacity, he expounded on the subject of evolution using neither script nor presentation aids. For the better part of an hour, he spoke of the study of evolution as a means of reconstructing the distant past, using the internal molecular clock embedded in the DNA of each and every organism.

Sydney was certainly no stranger to the field of evolution. Even as a student, he counted anthropology and palaeontology amongst his weekend pursuits. His passion for the subjects took him on field trips to various sites across South Africa, including a 1946 expedition into the Kalahari Desert, which led him to contemplate the ancestry of mankind in the paper *Man and the Great Kalahari Desert*.

In fact, Sydney's own research in molecular genetics followed a biological 'evolutionary food chain' of sorts. In his monograph, *The Food Chain of Research*, he described how he first worked on *Escherichia coli* and bacteriophages, which eat bacteria from the

BELOW
(From left)
Phillip Tobias,
'Buddy' Lawson and
Sydney Brenner
on a fossil dig at
Gladysvale Cave,
South Africa, in 1947.

inside; then moved on to the nematode worm *Caenorhabditis elegans,* which eats *E. coli* from the outside; then to fish, which eat worms; and finally to humans, who eat fish. With trademark candour, he concluded that "in the end, we are eaten by bacteria and worms to start the cycle again".

10-on-10 brought world-renowned scholars and thinkers to Singapore. Cosmologist John Barrow spoke of evolution as a byword for change, brought about by 14 billion years of alchemy and the expansion and cooling of the universe. Jack Szostak and Hyman Hartman had a spirited debate on the role of RNA and clay in the transition from chemistry to biological life.

How did all of Earth's biodiversity evolve from rudimentary protocells? Detlev Arendt described how single cells banded together into complex, multicellular organisms with a range of specialised functions, and Per Ahlberg took the audience on a tour of how vertebrates came to colonise the seas and dry land.

Our human origins have long fascinated biologists, anthropologists and archaeologists alike. Francis Thackeray laid out some of the most important fossil evidence for Africa as the cradle of humanity, and Svante Pääbo riveted the audience with lessons from the Neanderthal genome about what makes us truly human.

Homo sapiens is truly unique in its ability to use tools and technology to bend environments to its will; indeed, technology has now become inextricably woven into the fabric of our daily lives. W. Brian Arthur considered how technology evolves in a self-creating, combinatorial fashion, and Sander van der Leeuw spoke about the evolution of innovation in terms of how humans process information.

The lecture venues provided fitting backdrops that complemented each talk. In front of the massive tanks of the S.E.A. Aquarium, John Long and Byrappa Venkatesh took us through the changes in fish morphology and physiology that enabled the transition from aquatic to terrestrial life. From The Pod of the National Library Building, which offers a bird's-eye view of Singapore's cityscape, Roland Fletcher discussed how material artefacts have brought about large-scale societal shifts and the accelerating growth of human settlements, and J. Stephen Lansing spoke about the Anthropocene epoch, where human activity looks set to destabilise the planet.

10-on-10 took us on a scientific odyssey that traversed cosmology, chemistry, biology, palaeontology, archaeology, anthropology and sociology.

Institut Pasteur
25, RUE DU DOCTEUR ROUX
(XVᵉ Arrondᵗ)

Téléphone : 734 - 01-10

Paris, le   196

THE DOG ATE THE RCA TAN DWA SIS LAL LDAY

THE DOG ATE HER CAT AND WAS ILL ALL DAY
THE DOG ATE THE RAT AND WAS ILL ALL DAY

THE DOG ATE HER ATA NDW ASI LLA LLD AY

THE DOG ATE HER CAT AND WAS ILL ALL DAY

THE/DOG

The lecture series generated much interest not just within the scientific community, but also among young people and the public. At its successful conclusion, we decided that its powerful narrative deserved a more permanent record. The result is this book you now hold in your hands.

This book attempts to condense 14 billion years of evolutionary history and more than 33 hours of lectures and discourse into a single volume that is accessible to the general reader. In this respect, the highly talented editorial and design team of Shuzhen Sim, Oi Keat Lam, Rebecca Tan, Jeremy Chan and Juliana Chan at Wildtype Media Group have done a brilliant job.

Through this volume, we hope to provide some insights into how Sydney Brenner views the world around him, and in the process contribute to our own understanding of the world today and to our sense of who we are. Finally, we try to provide the reader a small glimpse of the future, by considering where evolution can take us.

Benjamin Seet
Executive Director, Biomedical Research Council
Agency for Science, Technology and Research (A*STAR), Singapore

TIMELINE

Years before present	Event
13,800,000,000	The Big Bang
4,500,000,000	Formation of planet Earth
3,800,000,000	Beginning of biological life on Earth
3,500,000,000	Single-celled organisms
2,000,000,000	Eukaryotic cells
900,000,000	Multicellular organisms
535,000,000	Cambrian explosion begins
530,000,000	First vertebrates
465,000,000	Plants begin colonising the land
460,000,000	Diversification of fishes
425,000,000	Coelacanths split from lobe-finned fishes
390,000,000	Tetrapods evolve and start to colonise the land
385,000,000	First appearance of copulation in vertebrates
200,000,000	Proto-mammals evolve warm-bloodedness
140,000,000	Placental mammals
25,000,000	Apes split from Old World monkeys
6,000,000	Human and chimpanzee lineages diverge
4,000,000	Evolution of *Australopithecus*
2,500,000	Evolution of the genus *Homo*; first stone tools
800,000	Human brain size starts to increase at a rapid rate
400,000	Neanderthals evolve in Eurasia
200,000	*Homo sapiens* evolves in Africa
70,000	'Cognitive Revolution'; emergence of fictive language
33,000	First cave art
12,000	Agricultural Revolution; permanent settlements
5,000	Earliest known writing; agrarian-based urbanism
500	Scientific Revolution
200	Industrial Revolution
The present	The Anthropocene; updates to evolutionary theory
The future	?

10^{10}

10^{9}

10^{8}

10^{7}

10^{6}

10^{5}

10^{4}

10^{3}

10^{2}

10^{1}

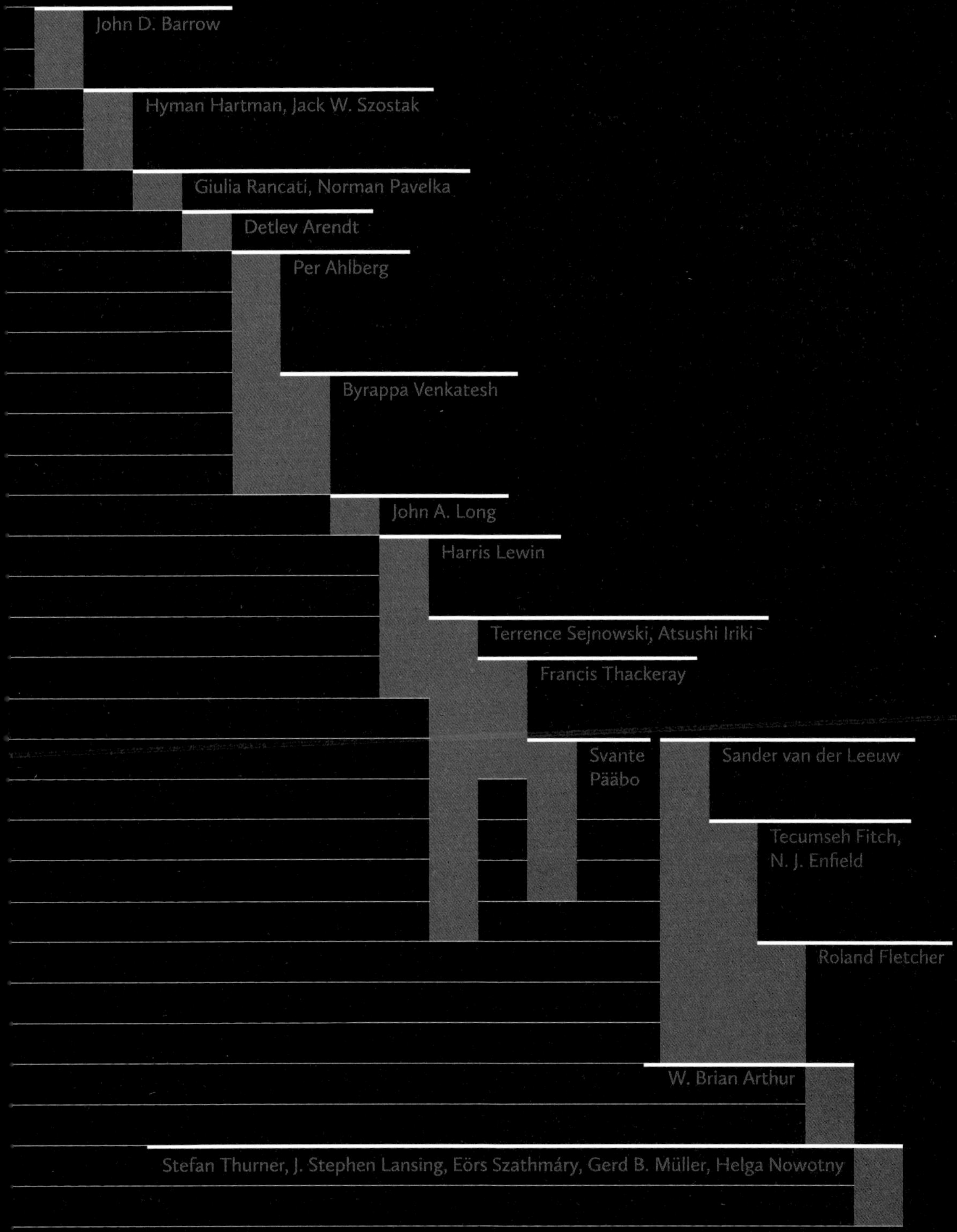

John D. Barrow

Hyman Hartman, Jack W. Szostak

Giulia Rancati, Norman Pavelka

Detlev Arendt

Per Ahlberg

Byrappa Venkatesh

John A. Long

Harris Lewin

Terrence Sejnowski, Atsushi Iriki

Francis Thackeray

Svante
Pääbo

Sander van der Leeuw

Tecumseh Fitch,
N. J. Enfield

Roland Fletcher

W. Brian Arthur

Stefan Thurner, J. Stephen Lansing, Eörs Szathmáry, Gerd B. Müller, Helga Nowotny

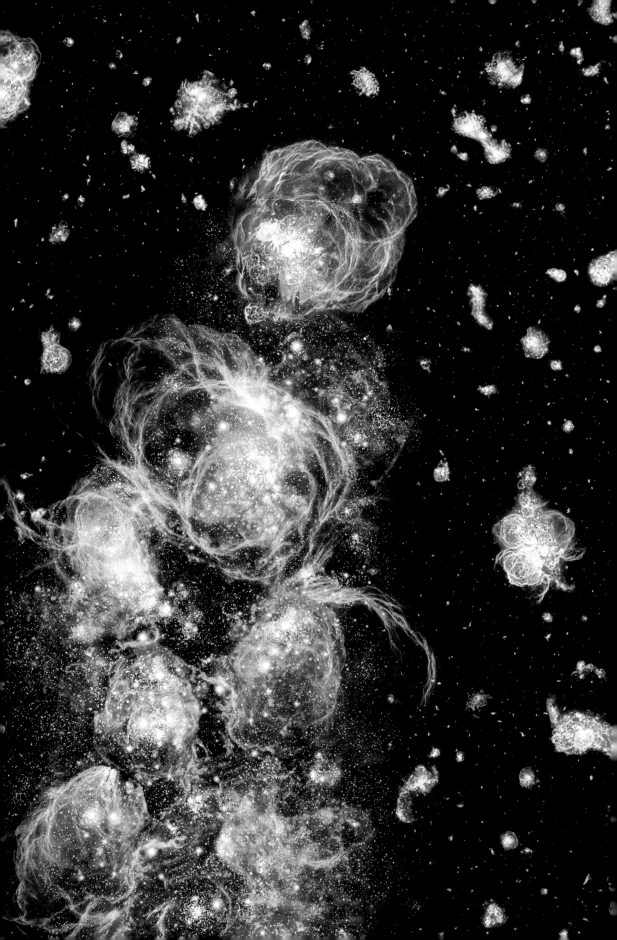

Chapter 1

Years before present
10^{10}
10^{9}
10^{8}
10^{7}
10^{6}
10^{5}
10^{4}
10^{3}
10^{2}
10^{1}

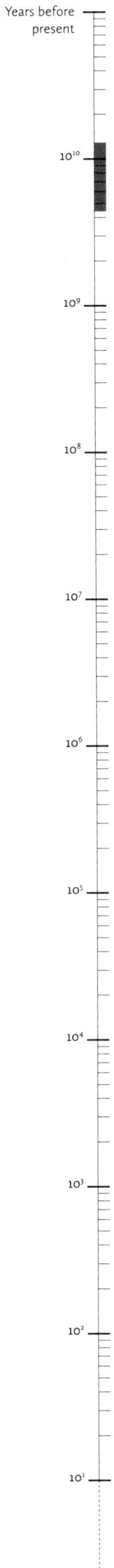

LIFE IN THE HABITABLE ZONE

Complexity in the cosmos

We live in an epoch of cosmic history which not only allows our very existence, but also offers us a unique and precious opportunity to understand the universe.

John D. Barrow

For thousands of years, philosophers, astronomers and scientists thought of the universe as rather like a stage setting—a fixed, unchanging space within which the planets, stars and other heavenly bodies had been set in motion.

Albert Einstein changed all this in 1915 with his theory of general relativity, which showed that space and time are in fact dynamic entities whose structure, rate of change and shape of flow are shaped by the material contents of the universe. Instead of a fixed stage, space is more like a trampoline, shaped by the movement of mass and energy upon it.

I like to think of cosmology before Einstein as a branch of art history. You could paint any picture you like of the universe—it could be cubical, it could be a giant cosmic pyramid, it could be a succession of turtles placed one on top of the other—and no one would have been able to prove otherwise. But what Einstein also did was to turn cosmology into a science, by providing a set of mathematical equations whose solutions (and there are an infinite number of them) describe entire universes.

Fortunately for us, our universe is very well approximated by particular solutions of Einstein's equations which show relatively simple behaviour, thus allowing us to make testable predictions about the nature of the cosmos and converge on the best solution of Einstein's equations. We have since learned a lot about how the universe evolved from a simple past into the complexity of galaxies, stars and planets we see today; along the way, we have also found unexpected connections between the properties of the universe and those conditions needed for life to exist and persist within it.

A UNIQUE INTERVAL

PAGE 20
Artist's impression of
star formation in the
early universe.

After Einstein, work by Georges Lemaître, Edwin Hubble, Milton Humason and others demonstrated that the universe is indeed in a state of overall change—it is expanding all the time, like a great lump of raisin bread dough in an oven. The raisins moving away from each other as the dough expands are the great clusters of galaxies that trace the cosmic expansion.

If we ran the clock back some 14 billion years, to a time just seconds after the Big Bang, we would find a universe many thousands of times smaller and hotter than the one we know today. Under these extreme conditions, only protons, electrons, photons and other elementary particles could exist.

> We therefore exist in a unique interval of cosmic history that can be thought of as a habitable zone in time, after the stars were formed but before they all go out.

Only after several hundred thousand years of expansion would the universe cool sufficiently for protons to catch hold of electrons, thus forming atoms and, subsequently, simple molecules. Over the next few billion years, some of this matter would accumulate still more matter, condensing (through complex processes we still do not completely understand) into stars, galaxies, galaxy clusters and ultimately planetary systems, including our own solar system.

From here on, the long-range forecast is rather bleak. Over the next 100 billion years, all stars, including the sun, will eventually exhaust their fuel and die, turning the universe into a great cosmic cemetery of dead worlds. We therefore exist in a unique interval of cosmic history that can be thought of as a habitable zone in time, after the stars were formed but before they all go out.

OLD IS GOLD

The very fact that we exist in this zone is inextricably linked to some of the universe's most fundamental properties, chief among them its extreme age.

As far as elements go, the early universe was almost exclusively made up of hydrogen and helium, with only minute traces of everything else. Carbon, oxygen and all the other heavier elements that make up life today did not appear ready-made at the beginning of the universe, but were forged in the furnaces of dying stars, where helium atoms combined via nuclear reactions into beryllium, then beryllium and helium into carbon, and carbon and helium into oxygen. By a remarkable quirk of the nuclear constants of nature, this production of carbon goes unusually quickly, but its burning away into oxygen is impeded.

These reactions, which yielded the basic building blocks of biochemistry, took billions of years to complete. Thus, we shouldn't be surprised to find ourselves in a universe that is 14 billion years old, since younger ones could not contain all the right starting ingredients needed for biochemical complexity.

Neither should the size of the universe surprise us; its immensity is simply a reflection of its age. In fact, we could not exist in a universe that is significantly smaller than the one we find ourselves in. While a universe the size of the Milky Way, with its billions of stars and planets, might seem a sufficiently large setup for life to emerge, it would be little more than a month old—barely enough time for you to pay off your credit card bill, let alone evolve complex life.

People often point to the vastness of the cosmos to argue that life surely must exist somewhere other than Earth. While this might very well be the case, the truth is that the universe would still have to be as big as it is in order to support even one lonely outpost of life.

THE PARADOX OF LIFE

The universe's enormous age and size have several other interesting consequences. For one, the universe is exceedingly empty—if you spread out all the matter it contains, you would find yourself with just one atom per cubic metre of space. This low density of matter explains why planets, stars and galaxies are separated by such astronomical distances, and why the universe is not swarming with nearby civilisations.

For another, since temperature falls in proportion to size, the expanding universe is now a very cold place, clocking in at just under three degrees above absolute zero.

OPPOSITE
US astronomer and cosmologist Edwin Hubble at his telescope in 1924. Hubble and others demonstrated that the universe is constantly expanding, like dough in an oven.

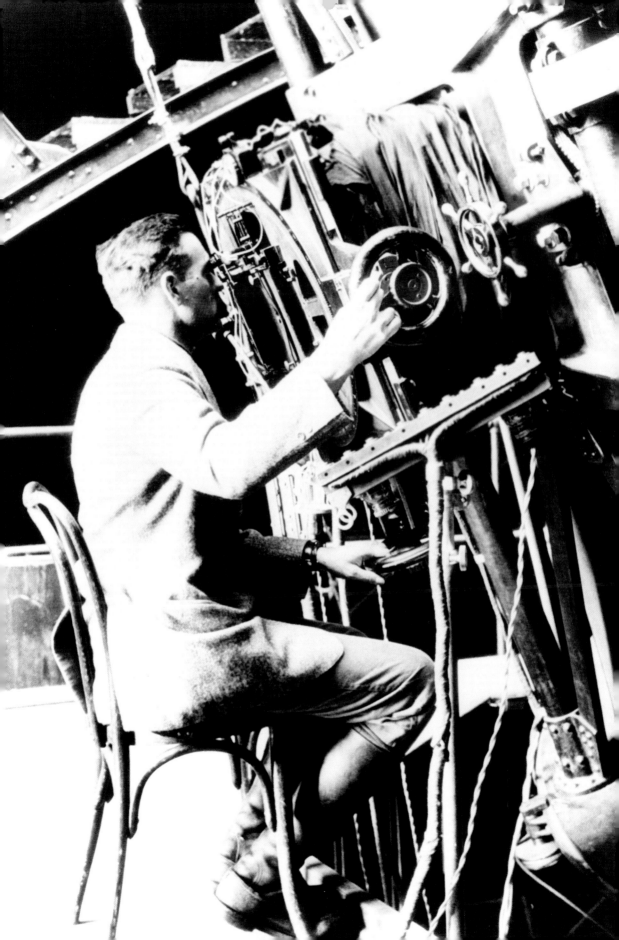

To develop the broad-brush
ingredients required for
biochemical complexity,
the universe must be old, big,
almost empty, cold and dark.

———————————————

Finally, despite the seemingly unending number of stars it displays, the universe appears dark at night. This is curious, because surely every line of sight out into the universe should end on the surface of a star, just like a look into the forest reveals a wall of trees. The whole sky should look like the surface of the sun all the time, and there should be no night. This 'dark sky paradox', which first puzzled 17th and 18th century astronomers like Edmund Halley, can be resolved if we consider that the expansion of the universe has reduced the density and temperature of matter so much that there is just not enough energy to illuminate the sky today.

Thus, we are faced with a curious, philosophically interesting set of consequences—to develop the broad-brush ingredients required for biochemical complexity, the universe must be old, big, almost empty, cold and dark. Paradoxically, these properties, which do not sound at all conducive to the evolution of living things, turn out to be absolutely necessary for the creation of the building blocks of life upon which evolution can act.

......

THE GREAT INFLATION

From its very beginning, a universe must expand at a certain rate in order to become habitable. If it expands too fast, falling far short of a threshold known as the critical density, matter will never cluster into stars and galaxies. On the other hand, if it expands too slowly and exceeds the critical density, it will collapse to a 'Big Crunch' before any celestial bodies can form.

Remarkably, our universe is expanding such that its density agrees with the critical density to within a factor of two percent today (making it what cosmologists call a critical universe, and what I like to call a 'British compromise' universe). Since any deviation from the critical value steadily increases with time, for this level of proximity to the critical expansion rate to be observed today, the starting speed of the universe must have been astoundingly finely tuned—it cannot have deviated from the ideal speed required for critical density by more than about one part in 10^{35}.

That our universe seems to be balanced on a knife edge is not the only bizarre thing about it. The expansion of the universe is also isotropic, meaning that it proceeds at the same rate in every direction. In addition, the universe is extremely smooth, but not completely so—it has a graininess level of one part in 10^5, just lumpy enough for stars and galaxies to form. Had the universe been just ten times more or less grainy, it would host no habitable regions.

In 1981, theoretical physicist Alan Guth proposed the idea of cosmic inflation, which offered an explanation for the universe's perplexing precision and uniformity. According to this theory, the universe went through a brief, explosive period of accelerated expansion beginning as early as 10^{-35} of a second after the Big Bang, growing from the size of an atom to cosmic proportions within a split second.

Though over in the blink of an eye, inflation would have many far-reaching consequences. For one, it would drive the speed of expansion up dramatically, launching the universe on the trajectory that drives it so close to the critical density that even 14 billion years later it is still tantalisingly close to the critical divide. For another, no matter how complicated, chaotic or turbulent the expansion of the universe was pre-inflation, the acceleration would drive away nearly all deviation from smoothness, leaving a slightly grainy universe whose expansion is perfectly isotropic in every direction to very high precision.

BUBBLES OF POSSIBILITY

What cosmic inflation—now regarded as the standard working model for the birth of the universe—also means is that the whole of the visible universe grew from an infinitesimally small region measuring just 10^{-25} of a centimetre across. But what about the rest of the early universe

that lay beyond that tiny patch? Parts of this could also have inflated in different ways over different time scales.

We should therefore think of the universe as rather like a great foam of bubbles, some of which have inflated a lot, others not very much and still others perhaps not at all. We live in one of those bubbles that has inflated enough, and over sufficient time, for stars and planets to form.

> We should therefore think of the universe as rather like a great foam of bubbles, some of which have inflated a lot, others not very much and still others perhaps not at all.

A prediction of this theory is that while the universe is very smooth and isotropic locally, it is highly inhomogeneous globally, and potentially completely different from what we can observe through even the most powerful of telescopes. If we could look beyond our visible horizon—about 42 billion light years away—we would see the expanded images of other bubbles, some of which might contain very different starting conditions.

Other extensions of this theory suggest that sub-regions of our own patch of universe could inflate further, producing copies of themselves that in turn will also undergo inflation. This unstable, self-reproducing process, dubbed 'eternal inflation', again changes our picture of cosmic history, making our visible universe just one of many inflating sub-regions.

So, the question of "Did the universe have a beginning?" now has a much more nuanced answer. Our visible portion of the universe had a beginning, perhaps when some sort of quantum fluctuation kicked off its expansion. But we don't know, and perhaps never can know, if the same was true for the entire multiverse of inflating regions.

OPPOSITE
Image from the Hubble Space Telescope of some of the faintest and earliest known galaxies in the universe. Some of these galaxies formed only a few million years after the Big Bang.

THE EPOCH OF UNDERSTANDING

The universe still has plenty of surprises up its sleeve. In 1998, astrophysicists led by Saul Perlmutter, Brian Schmidt and Adam Riess observed that far distant supernovas were dimmer than expected, and hence much further away than predicted by existing models of the universe. This led to the astonishing (and Nobel Prize-winning) discovery that, instead of slowing down under the effect of gravity, cosmic expansion changed gears a few billion years ago and is now proceeding at an accelerating rate.

What does this tell us about the future of the cosmos? Ultimately, it leads us to a rather sobering conclusion. At some point in the far-off future, the accelerating expansion of the universe will move matter away from us at faster than the speed of light, forming an unchanging horizon around us beyond which we can never see. Without historical records, astronomers of this far future age will know nothing of other galaxies—every one of the thousands of galaxies now visible to us will have receded beyond this impenetrable horizon.

So it is that today, we exist not only in a habitable zone, but also in an epoch of cosmic history that is propitious for the understanding of the universe. In this epoch, we can deduce the exotic history of the cosmos—that the universe is expanding, or that inflation occurred in the distant past—by observing phenomena external to our own Milky Way.

By comparison, astronomers hundreds of billions of years in the future might as well be in a black hole. Confined to their own little corner of the cosmos, they will find it impossible to make observations that will tell them about the universe's fundamental properties. For them, cosmology will not be a science, but a type of literary history. It is strange and sobering to think that in the distant future, the only way to learn about the universe would be to pore over old astrophysical books and journals from a long-gone era, when the stars were still within our reach.

John D. Barrow *is professor of mathematical sciences at the University of Cambridge, UK, and director of the Millennium Mathematics Project, a programme to improve the appreciation of mathematics and its applications among young people and the general public. He is a fellow of the Royal Society, the recipient of the 2016 Gold Medal of the Royal Astronomical Society, and the author of 22 books. His research interests are in cosmology, astrophysics and gravitation.*

This chapter is based on 'The Origin and Evolution of the Universe', a talk given by John D. Barrow on 21 February 2017 in Singapore as part of the *10-on-10: The Chronicles of Evolution* lecture series. The material here was abstracted and edited by Shuzhen Sim.

FURTHER READING

Barrow (2011) *The book of universes: exploring the limits of the cosmos*. New York: W. W. Norton.

Chapter 2

FROM CLAY TO THE CODE OF LIFE

Inside nature's biochemistry laboratory

The genetic code drives all biological life. But even a mechanism this fundamental rests on still more ancient biochemical processes, as well as the intriguing chemical properties of a seemingly nondescript material—clay.

Hyman Hartman

Years before present
10^{10}
10^{9}
10^{8}
10^{7}
10^{6}
10^{5}
10^{4}
10^{3}
10^{2}
10^{1}

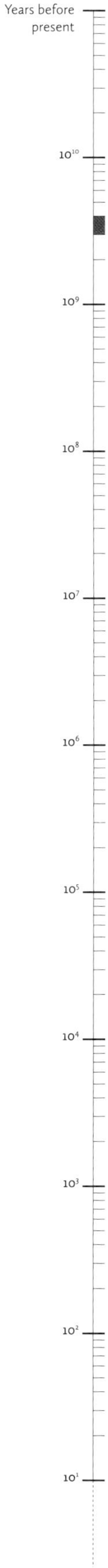

While many biologists today delve into genome sequences to understand how organisms evolved, the history of life on Earth is not written solely in DNA. Clues to this history are also inscribed in something far more ancient: metabolism, the intricate networks of biochemical reactions that make our cells hum.

Biochemical reactions are not only essential for sustaining life as we know it today; they were also central to its very origin some four billion years ago. Under the right geochemical conditions, the basic chemical building blocks available on the early Earth combined into simple molecules, which, over time, could be mixed and matched in various ways to yield increasingly complex structures. Some of these structures, simple amino acid chains known as peptides, had the ability to function like simple enzymes that were then able to catalyse the formation of still more elaborate molecules.

From this ever-expanding chemical repertoire evolved the molecules we are familiar with today—the full range of amino acids, protein enzymes, and information-carrying nucleic acids like DNA and RNA—and with them, the mechanism that lies at the very heart of biology: the genetic code.

> Biochemical reactions are not only essential for sustaining life as we know it today; they were also central to its very origin some four billion years ago.

A METABOLIC HISTORY

The genetic code is a blueprint for converting information stored in DNA—in the form of the nucleotide bases G, C, A and T—into amino acids, the building blocks of proteins. Each of the 20 amino acids is encoded by at least one triplet of bases, known as a codon. GGG, for example, specifies a simple amino acid called glycine, while ATC specifies a more complex amino acid called isoleucine.

We can look to metabolism for some clues to the origin of this complex system. Consider the citric acid cycle, an essential metabolic pathway for the synthesis of amino acids. Some amino acids require fewer steps in their synthesis than others—glycine, for example, is only one catalytic step away from the citric acid cycle, while isoleucine requires many more steps. This 'catalytic distance' gives us an estimate, or metabolic metric, of the order in which each amino acid entered the code: the earlier the entry, the fewer the number of steps required.

What we noticed is that early-entry amino acids tend to be specified by codons that contain only G and C, while later entrants tend to be specified by codons that also contain A and T. This suggests that, like a child picking up a language, the genetic code started out as a simpler, GC-only code involving a vocabulary of only a few amino acids. This vocabulary later expanded as A and finally T were incorporated into the genetic alphabet.

PAGE 32
On the early Earth, chemical reactions that led to biological life may first have taken place on clay minerals.

LESSONS FROM AN ANCIENT CODE

The origin of the genetic code is also tightly linked to the origin of how cells make proteins. In this process (commonly referred to in school textbooks as the 'central dogma' of molecular biology), information stored in DNA is copied into messenger RNA (mRNA) intermediates, which are then used as templates for the assembly of amino acids into proteins.

> This suggests that, like a child picking up a language, the genetic code started out as a simpler, GC-only code involving a vocabulary of only a few amino acids.

Amino acids are guided to the correct location on the mRNA template by hitch-hiking on adaptors known as transfer RNAs (tRNAs). These tRNA molecules recognise specific codons on the mRNA with their aptly named anticodons. But it turns out that there is more than one driver in the car. Independently of the anticodon, sequences in other sections of the tRNA can also instruct the cell to tack on a particular amino acid.

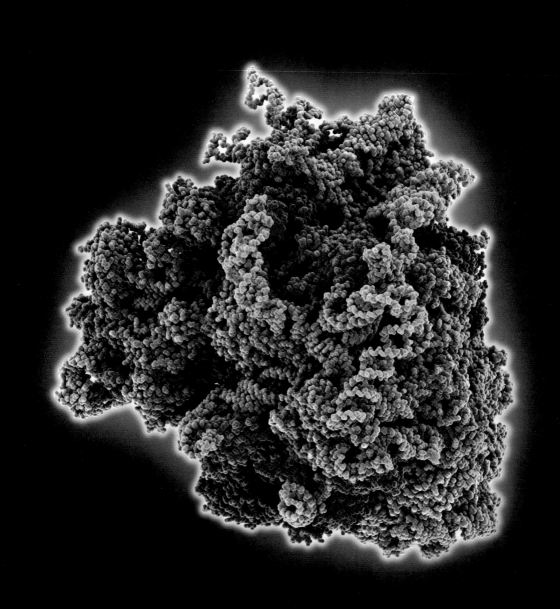

We think that these sequences, termed the operational code, are a relic of an early genetic code that functioned before tRNAs and other components of today's protein synthesis machinery evolved. In contrast to anticodons, which contain all four nucleotide bases, the operational code only consists of G and C—further evidence for an ancient, simpler genetic code.

READING MOLECULAR FOSSILS

In the cell, the assembly of amino acids into proteins—known as translation—takes place on ribosomes. These complex molecular machines are not only essential for life, but also form a molecular fossil record that we can mine for more clues to the origin of the genetic code.

A ribosome is composed of RNA intertwined with some 50 to 80 ribosomal proteins. But its beating heart is the peptidyl transfer centre (PTC), which carries out the task of chemically linking amino acids together. If we examine the proteins surrounding the PTC, it becomes clear that the ribosome as we know it today grew like an onion around this ancient catalytic core, incorporating it into the modern-day structure.

Like most proteins, those around the PTC are folded into a three-dimensional tertiary structure, but with a unique addition: simpler amino acid chains, or peptides, that extend off this structure and, in some cases, into the PTC. We think these short, simple peptide extensions were among the first proteins to be encoded and assembled by the early genetic code and translation machinery—a piece of evolutionary history preserved in the heart of the ribosome.

There are two lines of evidence for this hypothesis. First, the peptide extensions of the proteins most closely associated with the PTC—the centre of the onion—are enriched in amino acids that, according to our metabolic metric, entered the genetic code early on. As we move outwards from the PTC, late-entry amino acids become more common, suggesting that these proteins are relatively younger.

OPPOSITE
Computer-generated image of a ribosome from the fruitfly *Drosophila melanogaster*.

Second, the structures of the peptide extensions become more complex the further out we venture from the PTC, going from unstructured loops to more ordered forms such as the hairpins, sheets and helices we see in modern-day proteins. These more sophisticated structures require the properties of late-entry amino acids, and could thus only have arisen with the expansion of the GC code.

PEELING THE ONION—A THIOESTER WORLD

Just like the ribosome, the evolution of the genetic code can be likened to the growth of an onion, in that simple structures and processes that evolved early on were incorporated into the system as it became more complex. What we have been doing is stripping back the layers of the onion to reveal the inner workings of its core.

Let's go back even further, to a very deep layer of the onion. As we have seen, before information-carrying molecules such as RNA and DNA evolved, metabolic networks existed which, over time, generated a repertoire of increasingly complex molecules through a variety of biochemical reactions.

> What we have been doing is stripping back the layers of the onion to reveal the inner workings of its core.

At this stage, we think one molecular structure in particular was especially important for the origin of life: the thioester. Today, these sulphur-containing molecules are common intermediates in many biosynthetic reactions; importantly, they have the ability to link amino acids into peptides—a role they may have played before RNA, DNA and ribosomes arrived on the scene.

Thus, in this ancient thioester world, peptides were synthesised through biochemistry, without being coded for by DNA or translated by ribosomes. This concept also provides an explanation for a chicken-and-egg problem: the presence of peptides in certain enzymes' primordial catalytic sites, which we know predate the evolution of the ribosome.

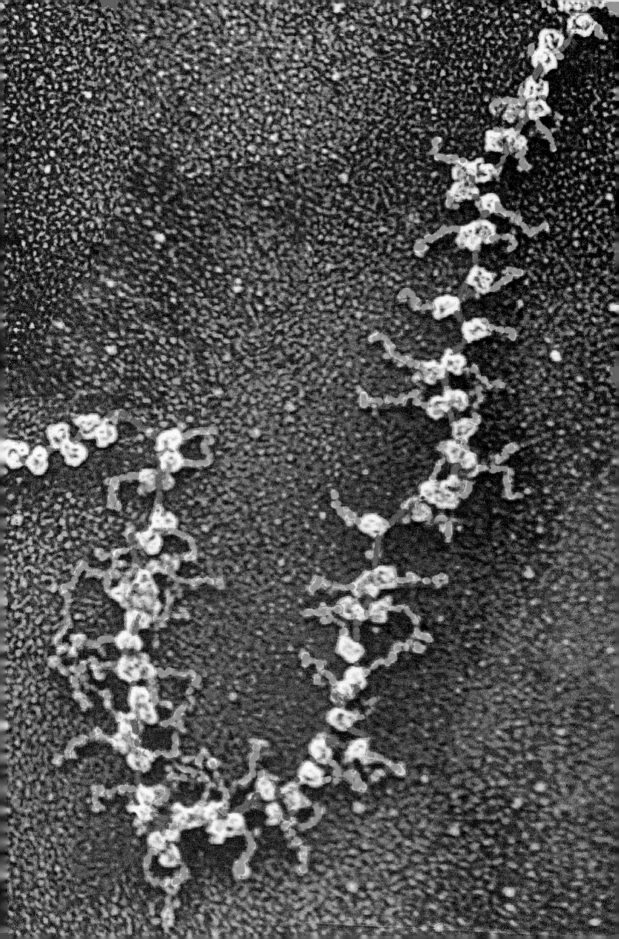

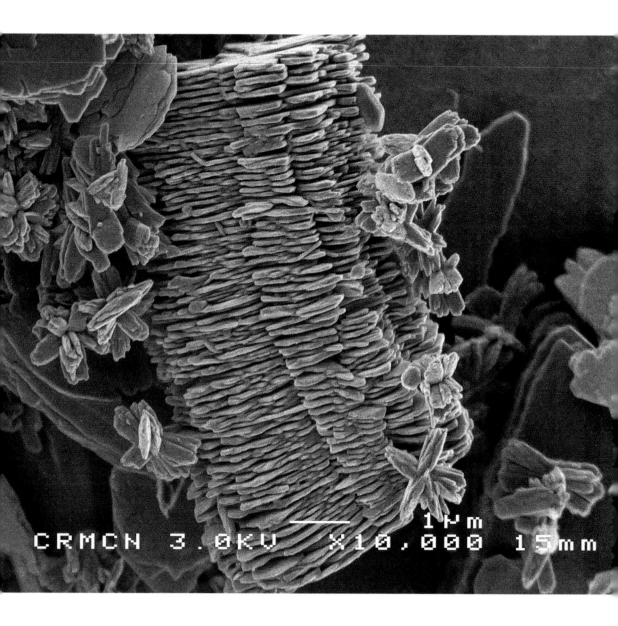

ABOVE
Scanning electron
micrograph of a
sample of clay from
an ochre mine.

......

THE CLAYMATION OF LIFE

Finally, let me take you back to a time before there even was an onion. Since only very simple chemical building blocks existed on the prebiotic Earth, what might have kick-started the process of biochemical diversification that eventually enabled the thioester world, the genetic code and life as we know it? Enzymes, which catalyse chemical reactions today, were absent, so we need a simpler mechanism.

We think the answer lies in a seemingly humble substance: clay. Formed through the reaction of silicates with water, clay minerals have layered crystal structures that provide ideal surfaces for molecules to bind to and interact with each other in close proximity. In fact, we have long used these very properties of clay to speed up chemical reactions in oil refineries and in the catalytic converters found in cars.

Thus, on the early Earth, clay minerals could have played the role of non-enzyme catalysts, helping to bridge the gap between simple combinations of atoms and complex organic molecules. At first, clay could have catalysed the incorporation of carbon dioxide in the atmosphere into organic molecules—a very early version of the photosynthesis we now see in modern plants. Over time, clay would then evolve the ability to incorporate sulphur, allowing for the formation of thioesters; nitrogen, allowing for the synthesis of amino acids; and finally phosphates, enabling the advent of RNA and DNA.

In the 1960s, the Scottish organic chemist Graham Cairns-Smith took these ideas a step further. He proposed that clay not only catalysed chemical reactions, but (much like DNA today) also stored and replicated information in the form of patterns in its molecular

> At first, clay could have catalysed the incorporation of carbon dioxide in the atmosphere into organic molecules—a very early version of the photosynthesis we now see in modern plants.

structure. Biological molecules could have formed associations with these nearly living things, later taking over and evolving into today's genetic machinery.

These intriguing characteristics of clay—which my colleagues and I continue to investigate—could tell us even more about the transition from prebiotic chemistry to the first biological life forms. Not only that—if life on Earth began in clay, this will guide our search for life on other worlds. When we scour the surface of Mars for molecular fossils of early life, we should look not only for amino acids and other biochemical molecules, but also for ancient minerals such as iron-rich clays and magnetite.

BELOW
Coloured scanning electron micrograph of magnetite, a naturally occurring iron oxide.

Hyman Hartman *is a research scientist in the Department of Biology at the Massachusetts Institute of Technology in the US. His work focuses on the evolution of the genetic code and cellular metabolism, as well as on the role that clay minerals played in the origin of biological life.*

This chapter is based on 'The Origin of the Genetic Code and Metabolism: From the Eukaryotic Cell to the Carbonaceous Chondrites', a talk given by Hyman Hartman on 13 March 2017 in Singapore as part of the *10-on-10: The Chronicles of Evolution* lecture series. The material here was abstracted and edited by Shuzhen Sim.

FURTHER READING

Cairns-Smith and Hartman, eds. (1986) *Clay minerals and the origin of life*. Cambridge and New York: Cambridge University Press.

Hartman (1998) Photosynthesis and the origin of life. *Origins of Life and Evolution of Biospheres*. 10.1023/A:1006548904157

Hsiao et al. (2009) Peeling the onion: ribosomes are ancient molecular fossils. *Molecular Biology and Evolution*. 10.1093/molbev/msp163

Hartman and Smith (2014) The evolution of the ribosome and the genetic code. *Life*. 10.3390/life4020227

Smith and Hartman (2015) The evolution of class II aminoacyl-tRNA synthetases and the first code. *FEBS Letters*. 10.1016/j.febslet.2015.10.006

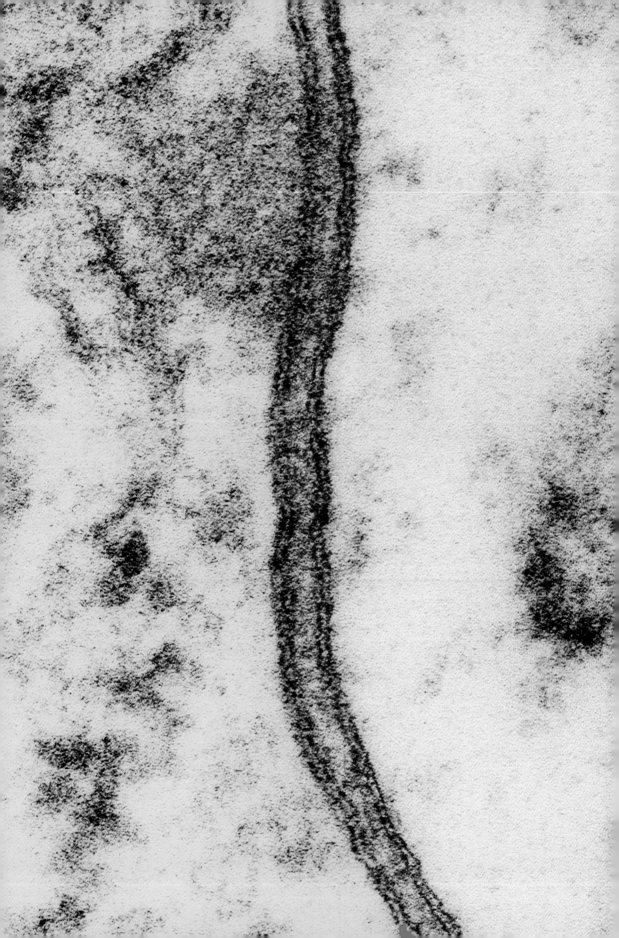

Years before
present

10^{10}

10^{9}

10^{8}

10^{7}

10^{6}

10^{5}

10^{4}

10^{3}

10^{2}

10^{1}

Chapter 3

STEPPING UP
TO LIFE

How chemistry begat biology

How did biological life emerge from chemical building
blocks on Earth? This is a difficult but not insurmountable
question, and an answer may well be within our reach.

Jack W. Szostak

Barring the invention of a time machine, we will never be able to travel billions of years into the past to observe precisely how life unfolded on Earth.

Yet, this doesn't mean that the first crucial steps in the evolution of modern-day life forms are forever obscure to us. It is possible to gain scientific insights into the origin of life—that is, how chemical building blocks gave rise to the simplest beginnings of biology, and then to the complex enzymes and metabolic networks that drive modern cells.

The question of how a chemical system became the subject and enabler of Darwinian evolution is a challenging one. Consider the workings of a single cell—information flows from its DNA 'archival storage' to RNA intermediates; RNA is then translated into proteins, which generate most of the cell's metabolic and structural complexity.

The problem with this system is that every part of it depends on every other part. You can't copy DNA unless you have RNA and protein enzymes, but you also can't make RNA and protein enzymes without DNA.

......

PERPLEXING PROTO-PROBLEMS

PAGE 44
Coloured transmission electron micrograph of cell membranes from adjacent neurons; the membranes keep the contents of the neurons separate.

OPPOSITE
Illustration of a ribozyme, an RNA molecule that can act like an enzyme and catalyse biochemical reactions.

These chicken-and-egg problems stymied the field for decades until the early 1980s, when Thomas Cech and Sidney Altman demonstrated that RNA can in fact act like an enzyme and catalyse biochemical reactions—it turned out that the chicken was also the egg.

This discovery (for which they were awarded the 1989 Nobel Prize in Chemistry) immediately changed our thinking about how life originated. Before the emergence of DNA and proteins, we think that RNA or RNA-like molecules carried genetic information while simultaneously functioning as enzymes for replication and metabolism.

If these RNA enzymes were free-floating, they would simply replicate unrelated RNA molecules. An enzyme contained within a

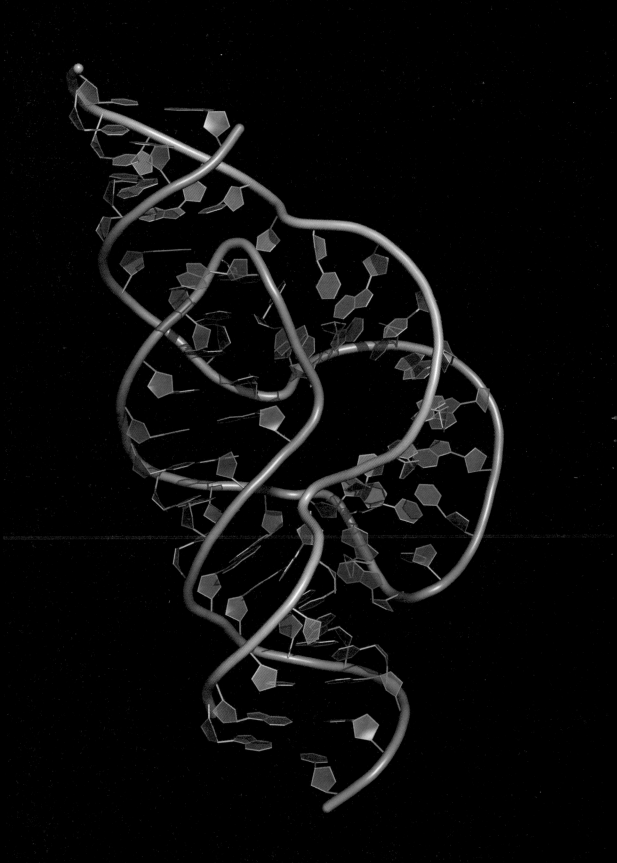

compartment, however, would replicate closely related ones. Hence, these molecules would have to be encapsulated within a membrane in order for Darwinian evolution to occur.

It turns out that putting primitive cells, or protocells, like these together is trivial—shake up some fatty acids in water at the right acidity, and they spontaneously assemble into bi-layered membranes, which then seal to form spherical vesicles.

The real question is how protocells grew and divided, and how they replicated their genetic material, in the absence of sophisticated biological machinery. All the necessary chemical building blocks, as well as the energy needed to drive these processes, must have come from the environment.

OPPOSITE
Illustration of a protocell, composed of a fatty acid membrane surrounding RNA molecules. Protocells enclosed genetic material in compartments, allowing for the replication of closely related molecules.

GROWTH, DIVISION, REPLICATION

Part of the answer surfaced when we used video microscopy to observe how spherical vesicles grow. The results amazed us: we saw the vesicles growing into long, filamentous structures, without their contents leaking out.

This unexpected finding actually solves the problem of division, namely, that it is very hard to divide if you grow as a sphere. A lot of energy is required to deform a sphere, squeeze out part of its volume and break it into two smaller spheres.

Filaments, on the other hand, are very fragile—a puff of air or gentle shaking is all it takes to fragment them into daughter vesicles. In a primitive environment, you could imagine that a gentle wind blowing on a pond would generate enough turbulence to cause protocell division.

This addresses the problem of growth and division. But for protocells to begin to evolve more complicated machinery, they also need to be able to replicate their genetic material in the absence of enzymes. One important conundrum is that RNA copying requires high concentrations of metal ions such as magnesium; unfortunately, magnesium ions totally destroy fatty acid membranes. RNA copying thus appears to be fundamentally incompatible with protocells.

There is a way around this. We found that certain molecules, such as citrate, bind to magnesium and mask part of its surface. This shields the protocell membrane while at the same time allowing the RNA copying chemistry to work. With this discovery, we were able to demonstrate non-enzymatic RNA copying inside fatty acid vesicles for the first time.

As citrate was unlikely to have been abundant on the early Earth, we believe that other molecules—simple peptides, for example—could have played a similar role at that point in evolutionary history.

FROM MEMBRANES TO MODERN MACHINERY

How did protocells then go on to evolve the sophistication and complexity of modern cells? For instance, while a protocell's simple fatty acid membranes are highly fluid and permeable, modern cell membranes are much less so, due to the presence of more complex molecules such as phospholipids, sterols and proteins.

A logical first step could be a protocell evolving the ability—in the form of a peptide or RNA enzyme, for example—to make phospholipids. But this ability needs to have a selective advantage, or it wouldn't spread through the population.

Indeed, we found that fatty acid vesicles spiked with a small percentage of phospholipids can grow in size at the expense of their non-phospholipid-containing neighbours. They do this by outcompeting them for fatty acids: at baseline, fatty acids readily move in and out of the vesicles' highly fluid membranes; the presence of phospholipids, however, stabilises the membranes and reduces the rate at which fatty acids exit. In other words, phospholipids make vesicles better at holding on to fatty acid molecules.

Thus begins an evolutionary arms race—the more phospholipids the cell makes, the better off it is, because it can outgrow its

> Thus begins an evolutionary arms race—the more phospholipids the cell makes, the better off it is, because it can outgrow its neighbours.

neighbours. But this can't go on indefinitely; eventually the cell grows to a point where the membrane's biophysical properties start to change, making it harder for useful molecules to get across.

It now becomes worthwhile, for the first time, to possess machinery for metabolism and membrane transport. At the start, this probably took the form of very simple peptides. But as membranes became more enriched with phospholipids, there would have been an advantage to making better and better machinery.

Primitive catalysts would thus have evolved into longer peptide chains and, eventually, the complicated, beautiful enzymes we see in modern biology. All these sequelae could have followed from a change in membrane composition.

> For many years, the complexity of modern biological life posed a huge obstacle to our ability to think rationally about its origin.

MAPPING OUT PATHS TO LIFE

For many years, the complexity of modern biological life posed a huge obstacle to our ability to think rationally about its origin.

We now recognise that it's often too hard to go all the way in one fell swoop to a final answer. But we can start by solving a problem in principle; this then leads us to an idea that is a little better and a little more robust. Eventually we work our way towards something that could have happened on the early Earth.

A scientific understanding of the origin of life thus involves figuring out a reasonable pathway of experimentally validated steps, going from simple and then more complex chemistry to simple life forms, and then on to modern biology.

If some steps are very difficult, it's possible that life is unique to our planet. On the other hand, if all the steps are simple and have a high probability of occurring, then we might conclude that life is probably abundant in the cosmos, and move forward with confidence in our search for it.

Jack W. Szostak *is a Howard Hughes Medical Institute investigator,*
professor of genetics at Harvard Medical School, professor of chemistry
and chemical biology at Harvard University, and the Alex Rich
Distinguished Investigator in the Department of Molecular Biology at
Massachusetts General Hospital in the US. In 2009, he was a co-recipient
of the Nobel Prize in Physiology or Medicine for his research into the role
of telomere maintenance in preventing cellular senescence. His current
work focuses on the origin of life and the laboratory synthesis of
self-replicating systems.

This chapter is based on 'The Origin of Cellular Life', a talk given by Jack W. Szostak on 13 March
2017 in Singapore as part of the *10-on-10: The Chronicles of Evolution* lecture series. The material
here was abstracted and edited by Shuzhen Sim.

FURTHER READING

Zhu and Szostak (2009) Coupled growth and division of model protocell membranes. *Journal of the
American Chemical Society*. 10.1021/ja900919c

Budin and Szostak (2011) Physical effects underlying the transition from primitive to modern
cell membranes. *Proceedings of the National Academy of Sciences of the United States of America*.
10.1073/pnas.1100498108

Adamala and Szostak (2013) Non-enzymatic template-directed RNA synthesis inside model
protocells. *Science*. 10.1126/science.1241888

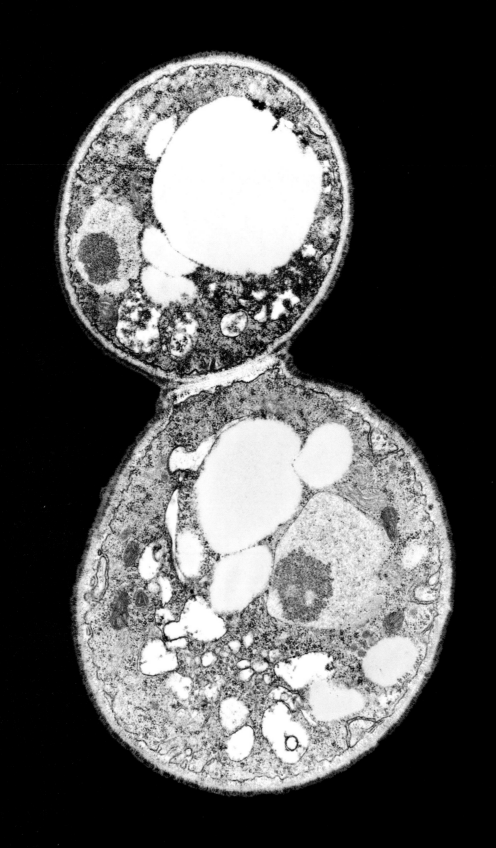

Chapter 4

WHEN CELLS GET CREATIVE

How modern-day cells evolved their complexity

By continuously reshuffling their genetic material, primordial cells progressively acquired more complex adaptations that allowed them to survive even the most unthinkable of challenges.

Giulia Rancati and Norman Pavelka

Years before present
10^{10}
10^{9}
10^{8}
10^{7}
10^{6}
10^{5}
10^{4}
10^{3}
10^{2}
10^{1}

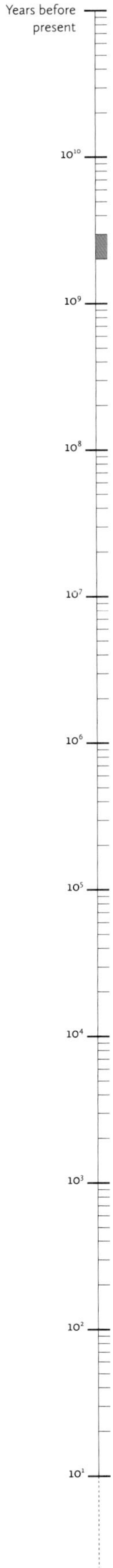

Today, all living organisms can be broadly divided into three domains: archaea, bacteria and eukaryotes. While archaea and bacteria are single-celled organisms that lack cellular compartments, eukaryotes comprise plants, animals, fungi and protists, whose cells carry distinct nuclei and other membrane-enclosed organelles.

Amazingly, all of this complexity and diversity evolved from a single-celled, microbe-like organism that lived on Earth some four billion years ago, known as the Last Universal Common Ancestor (LUCA). But how did we go from LUCA to the plethora of different archaeal, bacterial and eukaryotic cells that now cover the surface of our planet?

For starters, there was no shortage of time—four billion years have been more than enough to introduce countless changes, or mutations, into the genomes of LUCA and its descendants, and thus for evolutionary novelty to emerge.

FROM SMALL MISSTEPS TO GIANT LEAPS

The first forms of cellular life did not contain a nucleus to nicely pack away their genetic material in a separate compartment; in fact, they did not contain any subcellular compartments at all. Much like modern-day archaea and bacteria, their DNA was simply organised in a single circular chromosome, which more or less floated freely in the cytoplasm.

Because DNA polymerase, the molecular machine entrusted with the task of faithfully replicating the DNA molecule each time a cell divides, was not (and probably never will be) 100 percent fail-proof, small errors—called mutations—were (and still are) introduced here and there throughout the chromosome.

Most of these mutations did not bring any benefits, and would in fact have been deleterious to the cell's fitness. But occasionally, some of these changes improved the expression level or catalytic activity of an enzyme, or allowed it to work on molecules that it wasn't able to before. If environmental conditions happened to change in such a way that those mutations became beneficial, then you had all the ingredients for classical Darwinian selection to do its magic and favour the survival of the fittest cells. Eventually, many such small gradual changes allowed bacteria and archaea to conquer new environments (such as growing at an intensely hot temperature of 80°C or at a corrosive pH of 2) or to evolve new abilities.

Over the course of the next billion to a billion and a half years, bacteria and archaea evolved a number of amazing innovations, including the ability to manufacture glucose from water and carbon dioxide with the help of sunlight, generating oxygen along the way (a process known as photosynthesis). Other cells evolved the opposite reaction: the ability to completely burn sugars down to water and carbon dioxide with the help of oxygen found in the atmosphere (a process known as oxidative phosphorylation, a key component of aerobic respiration).

ORGANISING THE CELLULAR CLOSET

Around 2.7 billion years ago, our ancestral cells decided it was time to get things organised. First, the precious genome should be tucked away in a separate compartment called the nucleus. Then, highly specialised metabolic reactions, such as aerobic respiration and photosynthesis, should be carried out in separate organelles—mitochondria and chloroplasts, respectively. But how did the first compartmentalised—or eukaryotic—cell evolve?

> Around 2.7 billion years ago, our ancestral cells decided it was time to get things organised.

The prevailing theory postulates that an ancient archaea, most likely belonging to a superphylum called Asgard, engulfed an ancient bacterium that was capable of aerobic respiration. Somehow, the bacterium was not chewed up, and in fact survived and continued to divide inside its host. While the guest enjoyed a cosy environment with free meals all day, the host enjoyed tonnes of energy produced by its guest. An endosymbiotic relationship was born!

With time, the bacterium shed part of its genome and transferred it to its host's nucleus, and the two became dependent on each other for survival. Eventually, the host cell came to resemble a modern-day eukaryote, and the guest cell became a permanent organelle, the precursor of all modern-day mitochondria.

SEGREGATION ANXIETY

As cells became more complex, their genomes got larger. At one point, eukaryotic cells decided it was impractical (and perhaps too risky) to store all their genetic information in a single giant DNA molecule. The genome was thus reorganised into several linear fragments of neatly packed DNA, or chromosomes.

After this makeover, cells now faced two new problems during cell division. First, they needed to make sure that each chromosome was faithfully replicated into exactly two identical copies. Next, they also had to ensure that each pair of identical chromosomes segregated properly, such that one copy would end up in each daughter cell.

If you thought DNA replication was sloppy, far more opportunities for error exist in mitosis, the process by which cells ensure that daughter cells end up with exactly the same chromosome makeup as the parent. Chromosomes missegregrate all too frequently during mitosis, resulting in daughter cells with either too many or too few of them. This condition, known as aneuploidy, is usually not very well tolerated by cells. But occasionally, an extra copy of a chromosome is just what a cell needs to overcome a challenging situation—it could for instance encode genes that prove useful in an unfavourable environment, and having more copies of such genes means that more gene products can be made from them.

For example, our work has shown that budding yeast cells (*Saccharomyces cerevisiae*, a modern-day eukaryote) can survive a toxic

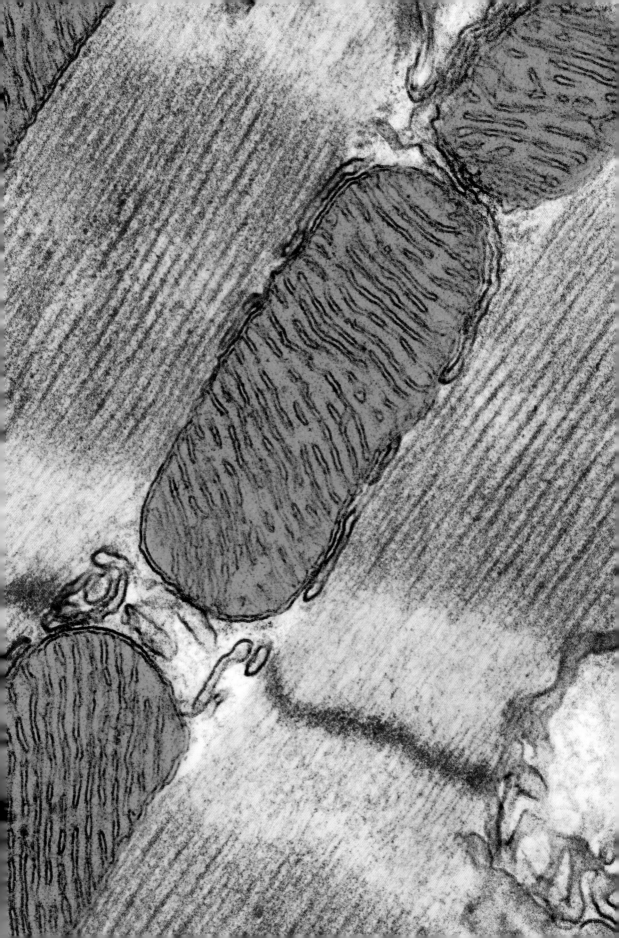

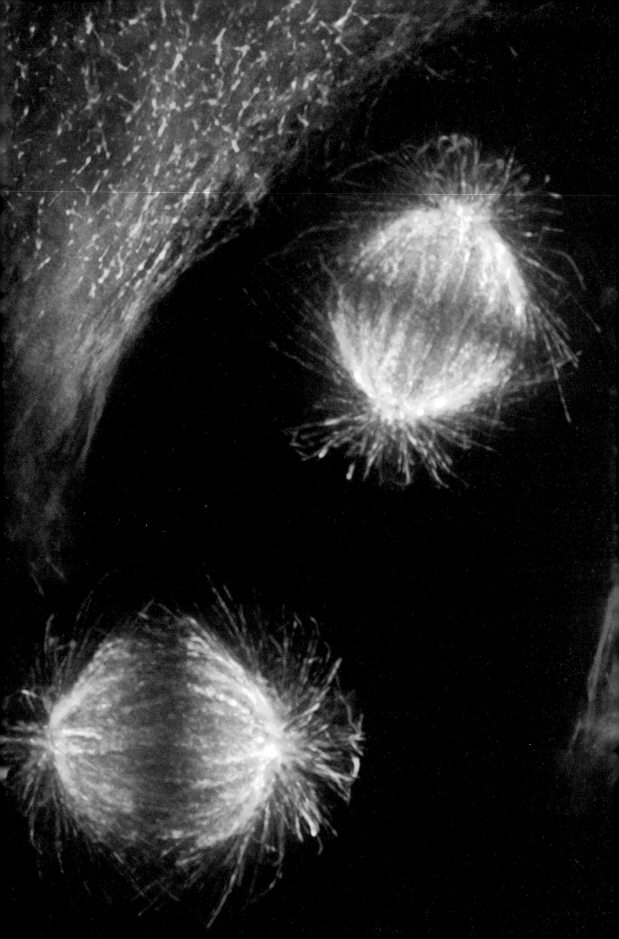

compound called 4-nitroquinoline-N-oxide (4-NQO) if they harbour an extra copy of one of their chromosomes. On that chromosome lies a gene called *ATR1*, which makes a pump that shuttles 4-NQO out of the cell.

MAKING DO WITH LESS

In life, however, not all challenges come from the outside. Sometimes, random mutations can disrupt the function of an important gene, such as one deemed 'essential' for the growth and survival of a cell. By definition, cells hit by such a mutation should not stand a chance. But our experiments have proven otherwise.

The yeast gene *MYO1*, for example, encodes a motor protein which tightens a belt-like structure around the middle of a dividing cell, pulling the cell membrane inward until two nascent daughter cells pinch off. This process, known as cytokinesis, is essential for yeast and many other eukaryotes. Yet, in work done in the laboratory of Rong Li (then at the Stowers Institute for Medical Research in the US), we found that if the *MYO1* gene is completely removed from the genome, yeast cells find other ways to carry out cytokinesis.

One way they can do this is through aneuploidy. Cells with extra copies of chromosome XVI, for example, also carry extra copies of genes for making the yeast cell wall—the meshwork of sugars and proteins that surrounds and protects cells. These cells were able to boost cell wall deposition at the division site, pushing the cell membrane inward to achieve cytokinesis without the help of *MYO1*. If you've lost your hammer, sometimes a rock will do just as well to get a nail in place.

> If you've lost your hammer, sometimes a rock will do just as well to get a nail in place.

Using a systematic genetic screen, we found that like *MYO1*, about ten percent of the 1,000 or so 'essential' genes in the yeast genome

OPPOSITE
Deconvolution microscopy image of cells undergoing mitosis, a process in which replicated chromosomes are separated into daughter cells.

are in fact 'evolvable essential', meaning that cells can withstand their loss provided they undergo a short-term adaptive evolution.

OF CHANCE AND NECESSITY

Thus, while most errors in DNA replication and mitosis lead to detrimental or even lethal mutations, some can open up new possibilities. In particular, while many random mutations in essential genes lead to their inactivation and hence to a cell's demise, they can also unleash rare adaptive compensatory mechanisms.

> Whether it's being thrown into an 80°C pond or having an essential gene inactivated, cells facing such life-and-death situations must either get creative or perish.

Although we currently do not know this with any level of certainty, we can speculate that many innovations that occurred during the evolution of eukaryotic cells might have arisen in response to severe stress conditions. Whether it's being thrown into an 80°C pond or having an essential gene inactivated, cells facing such life-and-death situations must either get creative or perish.

These rapid adaptations to seemingly insurmountable challenges can be witnessed even today. In fact, cells develop resistance against virtually any drug meant to kill them—see for instance the notorious ability of cancer cells to elude treatments, or the worrying emergence of antimicrobial resistance among pathogens. Studying how cells evolve adaptations to stressful situations therefore not only sheds light on significant evolutionary events in the past, but could also lead to strategies to prevent them from going down these undesirable paths.

Giulia Rancati (*left*) *is a senior principal investigator at the Institute of Medical Biology at the Agency for Science, Technology and Research (A*STAR), Singapore, and a principal investigator at the A*STAR Biotransformation Innovation Platform. She received the A*STAR Investigatorship award in 2010 and was selected for the European Molecular Biology Organisation Young Investigator Programme in 2017. Her current work revolves around understanding eukaryotic cell evolution and its relationship to cancer and the emergence of drug resistance.*

Norman Pavelka (*right*) *is a principal investigator at the Singapore Immunology Network, A*STAR, and also received the A*STAR Investigatorship award in 2010. His work focuses on the ecology and evolution of host-microbe interactions in the mammalian gastrointestinal tract.*

This chapter was contributed by Giulia Rancati and Norman Pavelka, and was edited by Shuzhen Sim.

···

FURTHER READING

Rancati et al. (2008) Aneuploidy underlies rapid adaptive evolution of yeast cells deprived of a conserved cytokinesis motor. *Cell*. 10.1016/j.cell.2008.09.039

Pavelka et al. (2010) Aneuploidy confers quantitative proteome changes and phenotypic variation in budding yeast. *Nature*. 10.1038/nature09529

Liu et al. (2015) Gene essentiality is a quantitative property linked to cellular evolvability. *Cell*. 10.1016/j.cell.2015.10.069

Rancati et al. (2018) Emerging and evolving concepts in gene essentiality. *Nature Reviews Genetics*. 10.1038/nrg.2017.74

Targa and Rancati (2018) Cancer: a CINful evolution. *Current Opinion in Cell Biology*. 10.1016/j.ceb.2018.03.007

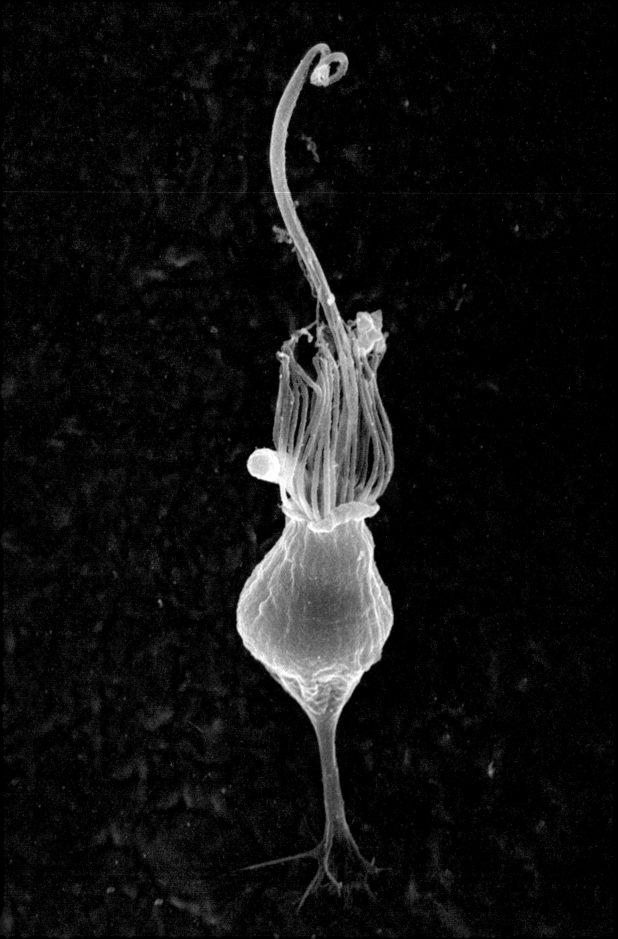

Chapter 5

FINDING STRENGTH
IN NUMBERS

Multicellular animals and the need for nerves

Complex, multicellular animals can trace their origins to a
single type of cell that gradually diversified into the many
types we see today, each with their own specialised function.

......

Detlev Arendt

Years before
present

10^{10}

10^{9}

10^{8}

10^{7}

10^{6}

10^{5}

10^{4}

10^{3}

10^{2}

10^{1}

After the first cellular organisms evolved, they enjoyed life as single cells for about three billion years. Although bacteria, algae and fungi all flirted with communal living from time to time, their multicellular co-ops were usually temporary and never became the dominant way of life. Being unicellular was sufficient and, in fact, an extraordinarily successful strategy.

It was only about 600 million years ago that multicellular life began to flourish, rapidly diversifying and developing radical new ways of living. This is the story of how simple single-celled creatures banded together and gradually became more and more complex—of how the first animals came into existence.

......

SURPRISING SINGLE CELLS

The story starts with free-swimming filter feeders called choanoflagellates, named for their distinctive collar-like rings of protrusions and long whip-like tails, known as flagella. Certain species of choanoflagellates are known to form simple colonies—balls of cells much like early embryos, not too far a step away from multicellular life.

As early as 1841, scientists noticed that the cells lining the insides of simple marine animals called sponges bore a striking resemblance to choanoflagellates. They thus named the cells choanocytes, after the filter feeders. Based on this structural similarity, we have assumed for a long time that choanoflagellates are relatives of animals, and molecular evidence now proves that this is indeed the case.

Genome sequencing has revealed a long list of proteins that are shared between animals and choanoflagellates. Apart from obvious candidates like adhesion proteins, which would have been necessary for cells to bind together, one of the biggest surprises was that choanoflagellates have many proteins

This is the story of how simple single-celled creatures banded together and gradually became more and more complex—of how the first animals came into existence.

that play roles specifically in the synapse, a structure that in animals is found in highly specialised brain cells called neurons.

This finding was unexpected. Obviously, single-celled creatures such as choanoflagellates do not have specialised neurons with synapses which enable fast neuronal transmission. Yet they already possess components that, later on in evolution, were assembled into the synapse.

STRENGTH AND SPECIALISATION IN NUMBERS

One of the main benefits of being multicellular is specialisation, which allows for a division of labour among cells. As single-celled organisms, choanoflagellates do not have this advantage; every individual has to multi-task, performing functions essential for survival, such

PAGE 64
Scanning electron micrograph of the choanoflagellate *Salpingoeca rosetta*. Many cell types in multicellular organisms are derived from choanoflagellate-like precursors.

LEFT
Scanning electron micrograph of an *S. rosetta* colony.

One of the main benefits of being multicellular is specialisation, which allows for a division of labour among cells.

as sensing the environment, capturing and digesting food and coordinating movement.

The evolution of multicellular life, then, is about the modification of choanoflagellate-like cells into many different types of cells, each with its own specialised function. In fact, if you look closely at the cells in different tissues, you will see that many cell types are derived from the collar-and-flagella structure present in choanoflagellates.

To study the origins of multicellular animals, we can take the choanoflagellate-like cell as the beginning of animal evolution, and trace different evolutionary branches by following the development of different cell types. Each of these cell types has a unique pattern of gene expression, switched on by a unique set of transcription factors.

In other words, we can take any organism living today, isolate its different cell types, analyse their gene expression through sequencing, and trace their lineage by comparing them to cell types we find in other organisms. This approach, called comparative transcriptomics, is what my lab is using to study sponges and other exciting marine animals.

OPPOSITE
A fossil sponge (*Vauxia gracilenta*) from the Burgess Shale in British Columbia, Canada.

BELOW
In complex organisms, choanoflagellate-like cells have been modified into many different types of specialised cells.

THE INVENTION OF NEW CELL TYPES

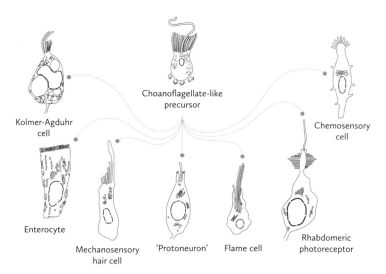

Kolmer-Agduhr cell

Choanoflagellate-like precursor

Chemosensory cell

Enterocyte

Mechanosensory hair cell

'Protoneuron'

Flame cell

Rhabdomeric photoreceptor

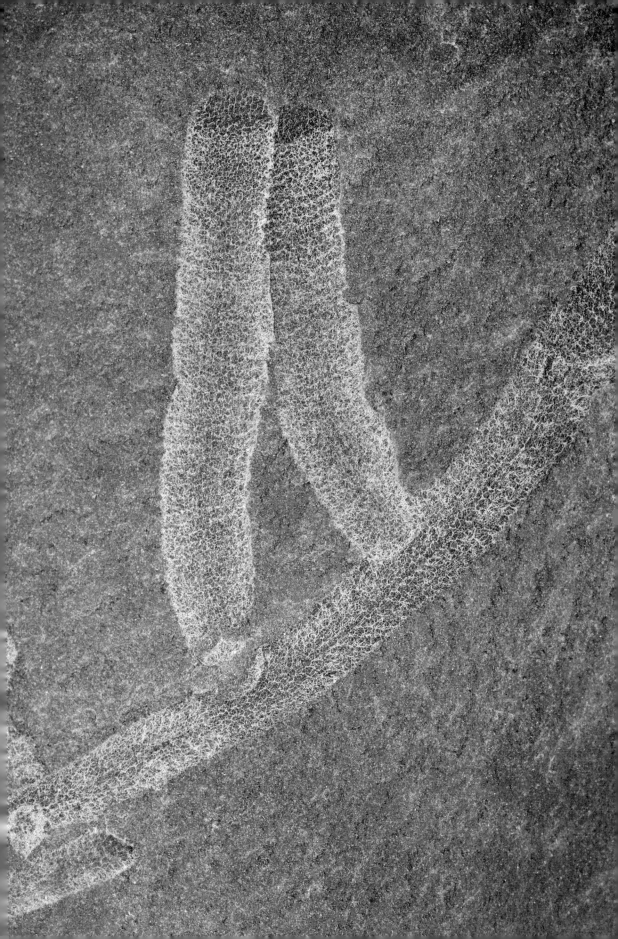

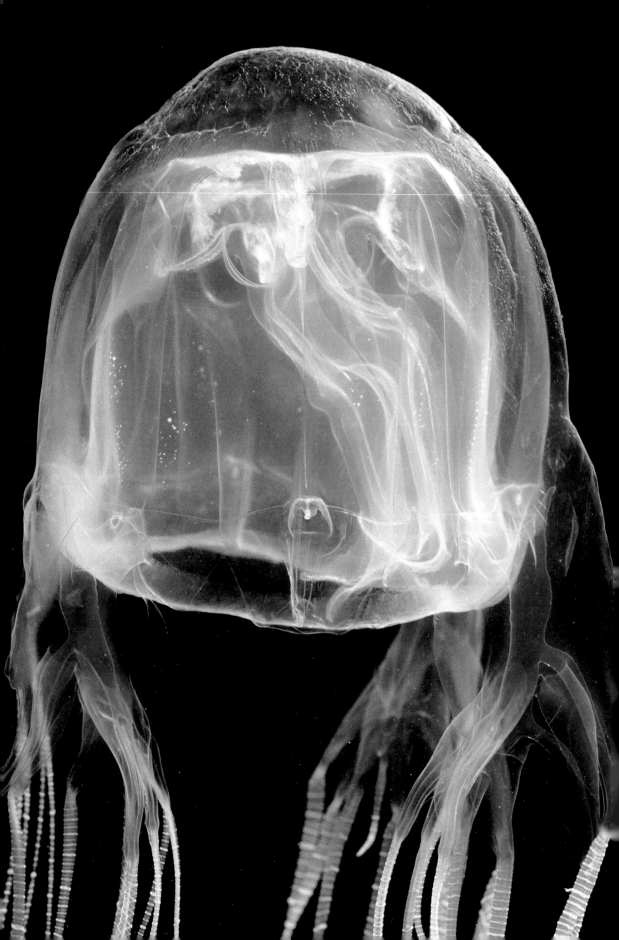

SLOWLY STARTING TO MOVE

A sponge can be thought of as a mass of cells—many of which are choanoflagellate-like—arranged as a two-layered cup. During embryonic development, sponges, and indeed most animals, go through a stage resembling a sphere which folds into itself, forming what is called a gastrula, effectively recapitulating what we assume has happened in evolution.

This idea that the history of the embryo (ontogeny) recapitulates the history of a species (phylogeny) was first put forward by German biologist Ernst Haeckel in 1899, and is now a hypothesis that we can test by studying animals at a molecular level.

We find that, like choanoflagellates, sponges also have proteins that are precursors to those found in synapses. While they are not full-fledged neurons, the cells that make these proteins already have the minimum capacity for what we would call neuron-like signalling. For example, although sponges do not have a nervous system, they do have neurotransmitters like GABA and glutamate for neuronal signalling.

Armed with this rudimentary system for intercellular communication, sponges can in fact move—albeit very slowly—through slow contraction waves. We think that over the course of evolution, these pre-existing features came together to form the first functioning synapse.

SEA ANEMONE INNOVATIONS

From sponges, which move so slowly that most people think of them more as plants than animals, we move on to the cnidarians, a group of animals that includes free-swimming jellyfish and tentacle-waving sea anemones. In these animals, the choanoflagellate-like cell has further specialised into neurons and muscles, among other cell types, giving cnidarians the ability to sense their environment and move much more quickly in response than sponges.

OPPOSITE
The box sea jelly
(*Chironex fleckeri*),
a member of the
cnidarians.

The major innovation in cnidarians was the nerve net, a diffuse network of nerve cells covering the entire body and coordinating the contraction of the muscles. Another important departure from asymmetrical sponges is the fact that cnidarians have radial symmetry, meaning that they are symmetrical about a central axis, like a cylinder or pizza.

But the vast majority of animals—apart from sponges and cnidarians—show a different kind of symmetry. Worms, fish and humans are all bilaterians, meaning that they have bilateral symmetry, with a left and right side that are mirror images of each other. How could this have developed from the last common ancestor of cnidarians and bilaterians?

If you took a cross-section of a sea anemone (a cnidarian), you would see inner foldings or gastric pouches with a bilateral symmetry. At the molecular level, too, these pouches are marked by transcription factors very similar to those seen in bilaterians. Based on this, we can speculate that gastric pouches eventually gave rise to segmented muscles and paired organs—defining features of bilaterians.

......

GETTING A HEAD IN LIFE

Apart from having to distinguish left from right, the first bilaterian or urbilaterian (from the German *ur* meaning original) had to make head from tail—quite literally. In recent years, there has been extraordinary progress in understanding how animals evolved to have a top and a bottom, and once again, our comparative approach has proved useful.

For example, when we compared the larval stages of sea anemones with those of bilaterian worms, we saw that similar sets of transcription factors were involved in controlling the development of the top versus bottom, regions we called the apical and blastoporal nervous systems. Our hypothesis is that the apical nervous system gradually moved from the top of the animal to merge with the blastoporal nervous system, fusing to form the bilaterian brain

OPPOSITE
A map of gene expression in the bilaterian worm *Platynereis dumerilii*, which shows bilateral or left/right symmetry.

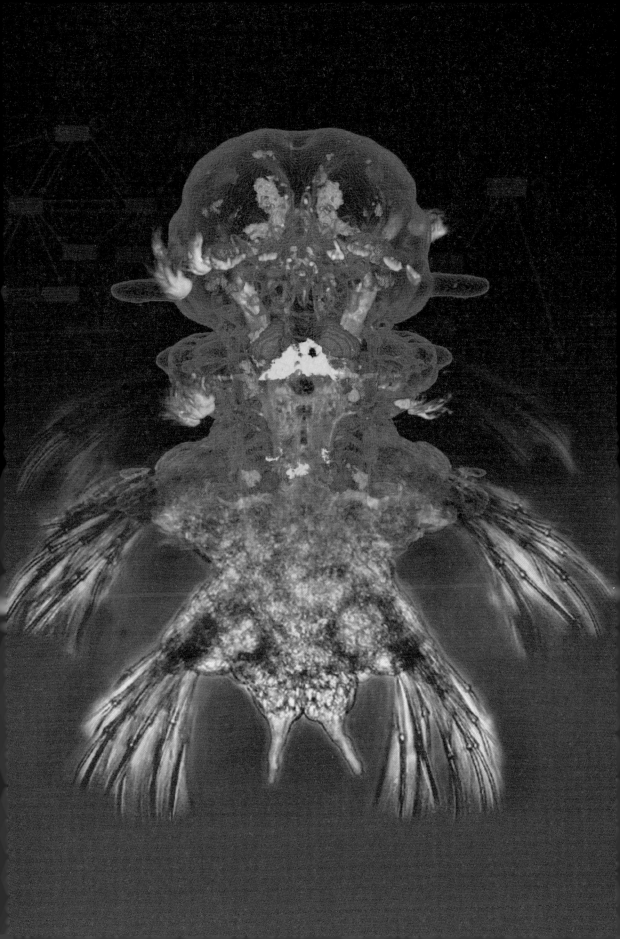

Apart from having to distinguish left from right, the first bilaterian or urbilaterian (from the German *ur* meaning original) had to make head from tail— quite literally.

housed in what is now considered the head of the animal.

Using comparative transcriptomics to study the bilaterian worm *Platynereis dumerilii*, our lab identified a cluster of genes linked to the apical nervous system, demonstrating that the apical region is a very ancient part of the nervous system that is already present in simple bilaterians. In *P. dumerilii*, these apical genes are involved in light sensing, responding to melatonin and controlling the upward and downward swimming of the animal. By mapping our gene expression data to a gene expression atlas, we were able to link each cell type to a specific location in the animal. Furthermore, by combining this information with imaging techniques like serial block-face scanning electron microscopy, we can even uncover the way nerve cells are wired.

Together, comparative genomics and imaging allow us to compare different cell types across very divergent species. We can thereby fill in the gaps in our understanding of how single-celled animals became multicellular and developed symmetry, eventually giving rise to humans.

With continued research into new atlases for other animals like mollusks and lancelets, we will soon have a good knowledge of the different cell types in bilaterian animals, and be able to compare them both within the organism and across different model organisms.

While all these advances mean that it is an exciting time for scientists interested in the origins of humans, evolution is not a ladder with humans at the pinnacle. After all, when seen from another perspective, humans are simply a very specialised outgroup to the cnidarians.

Detlev Arendt *is a group leader and senior scientist at the European Molecular Biology Laboratory in Heidelberg, Germany. His laboratory has established the marine annelid* Platynereis dumerilii *as a model organism for evolutionary, developmental and neurobiological research, and has pioneered the field of cell type evolution. A European Research Council advanced investigator since 2012, Arendt has also been recognised with the 2011 Kovalevsky medal.*

This chapter is based on 'From Nerve Net to Brain: The Rise of the Urbilaterian in Animal Evolution', a talk given by Detlev Arendt on 10 April 2017 in Singapore as part of the *10-on-10: The Chronicles of Evolution* lecture series. The material here was abstracted and edited by Rebecca Tan.

FURTHER READING

Tosches and Arendt (2013) The bilaterian forebrain: an evolutionary chimaera. *Current Opinion in Neurobiology.* 10.1016/j.conb.2013.09.005

Achim et al. (2015) High-throughput spatial mapping of single-cell RNA-seq data to tissue of origin. *Nature Biotechnology.* 10.1038/nbt.3209

Arendt et al. (2016) From nerve net to nerve ring, nerve cord and brain—evolution of the nervous system. *Nature Reviews Neuroscience.* 10.1038/nrn.2015.15

Arendt et al. (2016) The origin and evolution of cell types. *Nature Reviews Genetics.* 10.1038/nrg.2016.127

Marioni and Arendt (2017) How single-cell genomics is changing evolutionary and developmental biology. *Annual Review of Cell and Developmental Biology.* 10.1146/annurev-cellbio-100616-060818

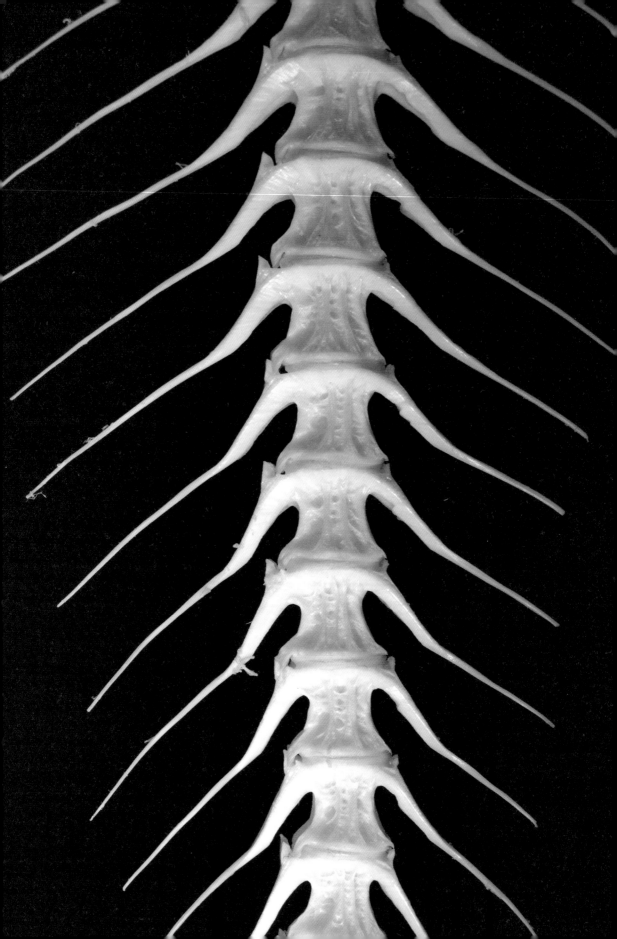

Chapter 6

10^{10}

10^{9}

10^{8}

THERE AND
10^{7}

BACK AGAIN

10^{6}

10^{5}

The sometimes circuitous path of vertebrate evolution

For all their diversity and complexity, modern-day vertebrates
are simply variations on a theme established during the first
100 million years of their evolution.

10^{4}

10^{3}

Per Ahlberg

10^{2}

10^{1}

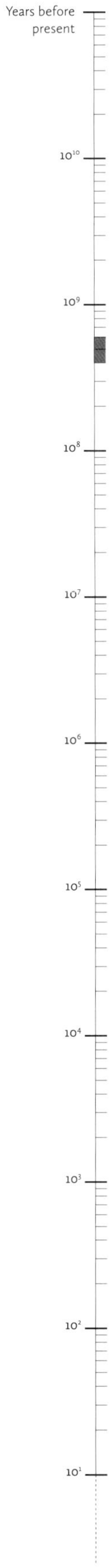

A leafy seadragon delicately floating amidst a bed of seagrass, a peregrine falcon closing in on a kill and a giraffe towering over the savannah may not seem to have very much in common at first glance. But in fact, they are united by a single evolutionary thread. Despite their enormous range of shapes and diversity in lifestyles, all three animals are vertebrates and have a shared body plan: a skull, a backbone and paired limbs.

The beginnings of this plan could already be seen in the first bilaterian organisms, which showed bilateral symmetry—that is, left and right sides that are mirror images of each other. This chapter will further trace the evolution of vertebrates, going from the first paired sense organs of the earliest known fossil vertebrates to the evolution of biomineralised tissue, and on to the subsequent great radiations that have come to shape the world as we know it.

A SYNTHESIS OF SOURCES

The very first vertebrates—species like *Haikouichthys* and *Metaspriggina*—started to appear in the fossil record over 540 million years ago, at the start of the Cambrian explosion. For us humans who live less than 100 years on average, this is more than five million lifetimes ago, well into what we call the deep past. How then can we say with such certainty that we know how our vertebrate ancestors came to be?

The answer is that we have data—in particular, we have successfully integrated two reliable sources of information to create a robust picture of the deep past: morphological data from the fossil record, and modern molecular biology.

Since the discovery of the genetic code, molecular data has overtaken traditional morphological data as a tool for reconstructing the relationships between different living organisms. Gene expression profiles of different cell lineages can allow us to draw insightful inferences about the deep past.

However, living organisms—for which genetic material is available for this sort of phylogenetic reconstruction—tend to be separated

ABOVE
Artist's reconstruction
of *Metaspriggina*,
one of the earliest
vertebrates.

from each other and their last common ancestors by hundreds of millions of years. Morphological data from fossils fills in these long evolutionary gaps, giving us crucial information about how the features we observe in modern organisms today first arose.

EVOLUTION ON THE MOVE

BELOW
Artist's reconstruction
of the early vertebrate
Haikouichthys,
which was capable
of swimming
and sensing its
environment.

In contrast to single-celled organisms that can move several body lengths within a matter of seconds, becoming multicellular at first involved a loss in mobility. Sponges, for example, traded in the free-wheeling single-celled life to become much more stationary communities made of many cells.

Even lancelets, the closest living relative to vertebrates, are relatively static filter feeders with no brain and no paired sense organs,

capable of little more than briefly escaping before burying themselves back into the ground. Fossils of *Haikouichthys* and *Metaspriggina*, however, show that the first vertebrates were capable of swimming and sensing their environment.

Although *Haikouichthys* was a soft-bodied organism, it nevertheless left a fossil that allows us to reconstruct a pair of eyes, nasal sacs and inner ears, suggesting sensory elaboration. Similarly, *Metaspriggina* has a distinct head on which we can pinpoint the location of its eyes.

Primitive though they may be, and perhaps unimpressive to the casual observer, both genera have an additional attribute that has proven very important in vertebrate evolution: a particular style of segmented body musculature that gives rise to the kind of stripes that we see in salmon steaks.

By firing waves of nervous impulses down their spinal cords and triggering sequential contractions in their segmented muscles, *Haikouichthys* and *Metaspriggina* would have been able to move their bodies in an undulating pattern and swim like modern fishes. As there is no counter stroke to work against, this method of locomotion is extremely efficient, and has contributed to the incredible success of aquatic vertebrates ever since.

> Towards the end of the Cambrian explosion, another major innovation occurred in one group of early vertebrates: biomineralised tissue, or bone.

BONE FROM THE OUTSIDE IN

The ability to move and make sense of their environment was a dramatic change for the first vertebrates, expanding the territory they could occupy and extending their range of options. Towards the end of the Cambrian explosion, another major innovation occurred in one group of early vertebrates: biomineralised tissue, or bone.

Although most people think of bone as an internal skeleton, biomineralised tissue first began as modified skin—scales covering armoured fish. Applying techniques such as synchrotron microtomography and electron microscopy to fossils, we can study the fine structure of these scales, revealing an astonishing amount of three-dimensional, biologically relevant information. For example, detailed scans have shown that the scales of an early vertebrate called *Anatolepis* are made of bone covered by a layer of dentine—the same material that human teeth are made of.

The predecessors of jawless fish such as hagfishes and lampreys took another route, their horny rasping tongues serving them well in place of biomineralised teeth. Meanwhile, vertebrates continued to experiment with bone over the millennia, fashioning jaws from modified gill arches and teeth from modified dentine scales. Sharks and rays subsequently abandoned bone in favour of a cartilaginous skeleton, but kept dentine in their teeth and skin.

In short, free-swimming vertebrates had become free-walking tetrapods by the end of the Devonian period, some 360 million years ago.

One particularly successful group of bony vertebrates were the teleosts, a branch of the ray-finned fishes that makes up 96 percent of the fishes alive today. Although much less numerous, the lobe-finned fishes such as coelacanths are an important part of the story of human evolution because they explain how vertebrates eventually took to land.

THE TETRAPOD TERRESTRIAL TRANSITION

Lobe-finned fishes like *Panderichthys* and *Tiktaalik* were among the earliest pioneers to leave the watery world and venture onto dry land some 390 million years ago, paving the way for the development of tetrapods, or four-legged animals. Although they still had fish-like tails and fins, they were in fact transitional animals that were increasingly interested in the aerial environment. Recent research has shown that their larger eyes, located higher on their head relative to other fishes—a feature that persists in early tetrapods—were an adaptation to aerial vision.

Panderichthys and *Tiktaalik* had strong pectoral fins that might have afforded them mudskipper-like movement over the land. But the first vertebrates to have limbs instead of fins only appeared later on in the fossil record; these had digits on their paired limbs rather than fins, as well as a large pelvis attached to the backbone that could support their body weight.

In short, free-swimming vertebrates had become free-walking tetrapods by the end of the Devonian period, some 360 million years ago. Once tetrapods established themselves on land, they underwent drastic physiological and morphological diversifications, the second great radiation following that of the ray- and lobe-finned fishes mentioned earlier.

BELOW
Artist's reconstruction of the lobe-finned fish *Tiktaalik*, one of the first animals to venture onto dry land.

To take advantage of the plants available on land, some tetrapods evolved to become herbivores, acquiring the ability to digest fibrous plant material. Others, such as the birds and mammals like bats, even took to the skies, adapting to yet another form of existence. Somewhat curiously, some tetrapods—such as whales—have also gone back into the seas, becoming an important part of the oceanic ecosystem.

COMING FULL CIRCLE

Despite all the anatomical transformations that vertebrates have gone through since leaving the seas, these relatively recent changes were nowhere near as radical as what happened within the first 100 million years of vertebrate evolution, which created a truly novel animal with sensory, cognitive and locomotion capabilities far beyond those of its filter-feeding ancestors.

Once the basic vertebrate body plan was put in place, all subsequent evolution has involved adapting this basic plan to different lifestyles and environments. Although there have been major physiological, morphological and behavioural changes, the time of grand anatomical innovation seems to be over.

Vertebrate evolution, like that of any other group, is not a story of linear progress, as Darwin rightly recognised in his very first phylogenetic tree. In fact, sometimes, evolution may even bring us on a somewhat circular journey.

Take for example the largest animal on the planet today, the blue whale. As a tetrapod, it is the product of a very complicated evolutionary history. It has biomineralised tissue, a big brain, paired appendages and other hallmarks of an advanced tetrapod. And yet when it dies, it falls to the bottom of the ocean and is consumed by scores of hagfish, the most basal member of the vertebrates still alive.

In a further twist, for all its long evolutionary history and sophistication, the blue whale is essentially a free-swimming filter feeder—one that has retrieved and repurposed a mode of life that was first seen at the very beginning of vertebrate evolution.

Per Ahlberg *is a professor of evolutionary organismal biology*
at Uppsala University, Sweden, where he researches vertebrate
palaeontology, developmental biology and genomics. Prior to his
appointment at Uppsala University in 2003, he held positions at the
Natural History Museum in London and the University of Oxford.
In 2012, Ahlberg was elected to the Royal Swedish Academy of Sciences.

This chapter is based on 'The Origin and Early Evolution of Vertebrates: From Jawless Wonders
to the Conquest of the Land', a talk given by Per Ahlberg on 10 April 2017 in Singapore as part
of the *10-on-10: The Chronicles of Evolution* lecture series. The material here was abstracted and
edited by Rebecca Tan.

FURTHER READING

Ahlberg, ed. (2001) *Major events in early vertebrate evolution: paleontology, phylogeny, genetics and
development*. London: Taylor and Francis.

Boisvert et al. (2008) The pectoral fin of *Panderichthys* and the origin of digits. *Nature*.
10.1038/nature07339

Clement and Ahlberg (2014) The first virtual cranial endocast of a lungfish (Sarcopterygii: Dipnoi),
PLoS One. 10.1371/journal.pone.0113898

Qu et al. (2015) Three-dimensional virtual histology of Silurian osteostracan scales revealed by
synchrotron radiation microtomography. *Journal of Morphology*. 10.1002/jmor.20386

Sanchez et al. (2016) Life history of the stem tetrapod *Acanthostega* revealed by synchrotron
microtomography. *Nature*. 10.1038/nature19354

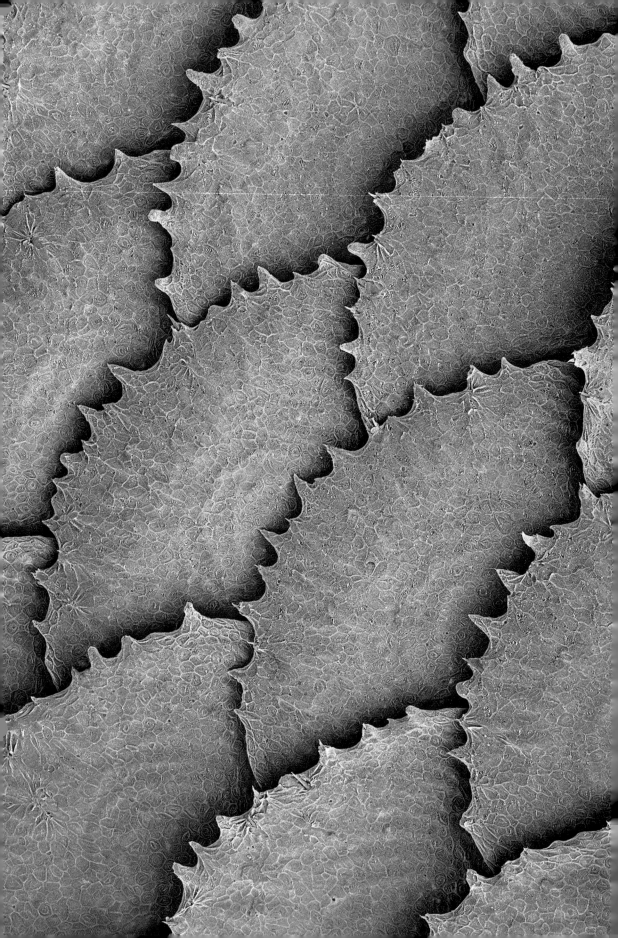

Chapter 7

CONQUEST OF THE LAND AND SEA

The explosive evolution of fish

Because humans can be thought of as a highly modified form of bony fish, the story of fish evolution is part of our own evolutionary history.

Byrappa Venkatesh

Years before present
10^{10}
10^{9}
10^{8}
10^{7}
10^{6}
10^{5}
10^{4}
10^{3}
10^{2}
10^{1}

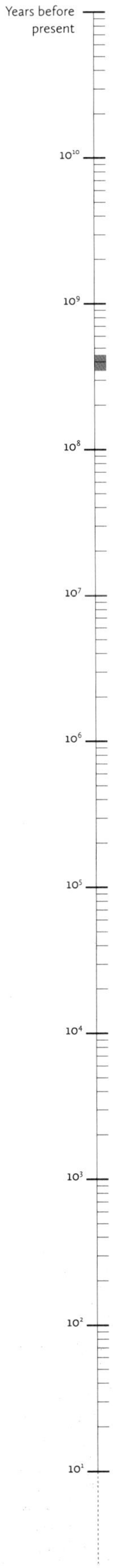

As far as animals with backbones go, no class of vertebrates is as wonderfully diverse as fishes. Take for example the longest known fish in the world, the giant oarfish, which at 17 metres is more than 200 times longer than the smallest fish in the world, the eight-millimetre-long *Paedocypris progenetica*. Size aside, fish lifetimes also vary wildly, ranging from the pygmy goby which lives for at most two months to the Greenland shark which lives an average of 400 years.

Their dazzling array of forms and lifestyles has made fishes extraordinarily successful, allowing them to colonise a wide variety of niches. In fact, just one group of ray-finned fishes—the teleosts—alone accounts for nearly 50 percent of all the vertebrates alive in the world today, with species numbering over 30,000.

While fishes are the undisputed masters of the sea, not many people realise that they have also indirectly colonised the land as well.

FISHES ARE FAMILY

While fishes are the undisputed masters of the sea, not many people realise that they have also indirectly colonised the land as well, through a particular branch called the lobe-finned fishes, the direct ancestors of all four-limbed animals—including ourselves.

Although lobe-finned fishes like lungfish and coelacanths may superficially resemble 'regular' fish like eels and groupers, they are actually more closely related to humans and other mammals. Their fleshy, limb-like fins—markedly different from the fan-like fins of teleosts—are analogous to our arms and legs.

For this reason, humans are grouped under the same taxon as lobe-finned fishes, making us one type of bony fish. Our evolutionary history is rooted in fishes; to understand the evolution of humans, therefore, we need to first study the evolution of fishes.

PAGE 86
Coloured scanning electron micrograph of cichlid fish scales.

BELOW
The coelacanth's limb-like fins are analogous to human arms and legs.

......

WHY DID FISHES EVOLVE SO FAST?

One of the major puzzles about the evolution of fishes is how they diversified into such a large number of species, with remarkable variation in their morphology, colouration, behaviour and habitat.

In the plant kingdom, a doubling of the entire genome is thought to have allowed the rapid diversification of flowering plants, which are the most diverse group of land plants and account for approximately 80 percent of all green plants in existence today. Since whole genome duplication has also occurred in teleosts, the most species-rich group of fishes, it has been proposed as the driver of diversification in fishes. However, there are a number of pieces of the puzzle that don't quite fit.

First, if you look closely at how teleost species have diversified, you will notice that the rate of diversification has not been very uniform. Whole genome duplication occurred early on in teleost evolution but only two groups of teleosts—Ostariophysi and Percomorpha—have shown hyperdiversification, together accounting for more than 80 percent of all teleost fishes alive today.

Furthermore, there was a long time lag between whole genome duplication and the diversification of teleosts. After whole genome duplication occurred around 400 million years ago, more than 100 million years passed before the diversification of Ostariophysi took place. Percomorpha diversification was even more recent, happening only 100 million years ago.

Cichlid fishes—the most diverse group of freshwater fishes— are yet another challenge to the hypothesis that whole genome duplication drove diversification in fishes. Cichlids, which are textbook examples of adaptive radiation and explosive speciation, did not have a whole genome duplication event in their recent ancestors.

But when we analysed their genomes, we found that both the protein-coding sequences and regulatory regions of cichlid DNA were evolving faster than normal. We also found an increased frequency of gene duplication in cichlid lineages; intriguingly, more than 20 percent of newly duplicated genes exhibited a new

OPPOSITE
The cichlid fish
Cyphotilapia
frontosa. Cichlids
are textbook
examples
of adaptive
radiation, yet
their recent
ancestors did not
undergo genome
duplication.

expression pattern, meaning that they started expressing in a new tissue or domain, giving rise to a new function and probably a new phenotype.

ANSWERS FROM THE EXTREMES

A major strategy for understanding the genetic basis of phenotypic variation in fishes is to study the genomes of extreme phenotypes, highly specialised fishes that have radically departed from the typical body plan seen in most fish.

If you think of the different shapes that fishes take as a continuum of variation from one species to another, seahorses are at the extreme end of the scale of specialisation. The first and most obvious difference is that seahorses swim upright, unlike other fishes that swim horizontally.

The first and most obvious difference is that seahorses swim upright, unlike other fishes that swim horizontally.

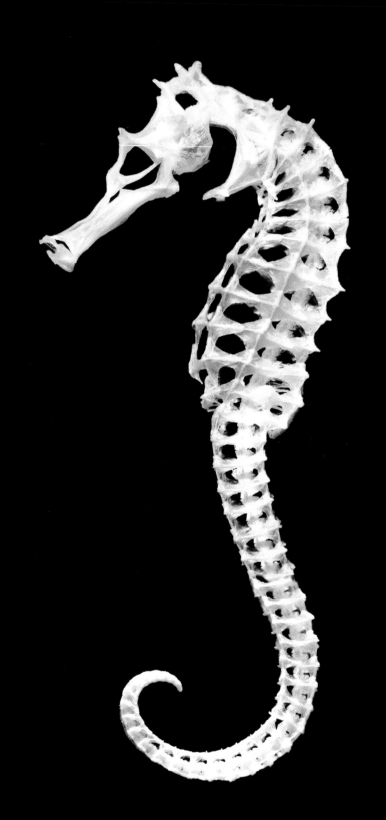

Seahorses have no pelvic fins (the equivalent of our hind limbs). Neither do they have scales; instead, their entire body is covered with bony plates all the way from the jaw to the tip of the tail.

But seahorses are perhaps most famous for their reversal of roles when it comes to reproduction. During mating, the female transfers eggs into a specialised structure on the male called the brood pouch, which is functionally equivalent to the uterus in mammals. At the end of the pregnancy, the male gives birth to anywhere from 20 to 1,000 fully formed young seahorses.

When we sequenced the genome of the tiger tail seahorse (*Hippocampus comes*), we found that it was evolving even faster than cichlids, leading us to suggest that the high turnover of nucleotides has allowed seahorses to develop their highly specialised phenotype.

We also found that seahorses had completely lost a gene known to be important for the development of pelvic fins or hind limbs, *tbx4*. When we used CRISPR-Cas9 gene editing to introduce mutations into this gene in laboratory zebrafish, they completely lost their pelvic fins, suggesting that the loss of *tbx4* was responsible for the loss of pelvic fins in seahorses.

OPPOSITE
A seahorse skeleton showing the bony plates that cover its body.

MAKING THE TERRESTRIAL TRANSITION

The transition [to dry land], however, was by no means trivial, requiring drastic changes to morphology, anatomy and physiology.

While the ray-finned fishes were establishing their dominance in the ocean, the lobe-finned fishes were slowly making their way to dry land where there was abundant food, little competition and virtually no predators. The transition, however, was by no means trivial, requiring drastic changes to morphology, anatomy and physiology.

One of these changes was the fin-to-limb transition, which enabled land animals to raise themselves above the ground and move freely on land to explore the terrestrial environment. To better understand how the descendants of lobe-finned fishes made this transition, we compared the genome of the coelacanth, a lobe-finned fish, with the genomes of other animals.

The comparison led us to discover a sequence of non-coding, regulatory DNA that both coelacanths and land animals had but that was missing in fishes. When we extracted this regulatory DNA sequence from the coelacanth genome and introduced it into mice, it was active in the regions that give rise to the wrist and fingers, which are structures found in land animals but absent in both fishes and coelacanths.

What these results suggest is that this coelacanth regulatory DNA allowed the descendants of coelacanths to start evolving land animal limbs, gradually adding on more genes that eventually gave rise to the wrist and fingers. In this respect, the coelacanth is an intermediary between aquatic and terrestrial animals, and a major inflection point in the evolution of vertebrates.

> As Sydney Brenner famously said in his Nobel Prize acceptance speech, these different life forms are nature's gift to science.

TAKING ADVANTAGE OF NATURE'S EXPERIMENTS

Ultimately, the large diversity we see in fishes is attributable to nature's experiments. Nature seems to have carried out a massive random mutagenic experiment, creating thousands of different lines and passing them through selection over hundreds of millions of years.

As Sydney Brenner famously said in his Nobel Prize acceptance speech, these different life forms are nature's gift to science. It's up to us scientists to interrogate these genomes and unlock their secrets.

The cost of DNA sequencing has come down so much that it is now affordable to sequence virtually any genome. We now also have tools that allow us to easily and accurately modify the genomes of model species, so that we can test our ideas in the lab. All these advances make comparative genomics a very powerful approach for understanding the genetic basis of the rich diversity of life on Earth—both on land and in the seas.

Byrappa Venkatesh *is a professor and research director at the Institute of Molecular and Cell Biology at Singapore's Agency for Science, Technology and Research. Venkatesh returned to Singapore in 1992 after completing his post-doctoral studies with Nobel laureate Sydney Brenner at the Medical Research Council, UK. In addition to his research on comparative genomics, he is a chairperson of Genome 10K, a project that aims to sequence the genomes of 10,000 vertebrates.*

This chapter is based on 'Evolution and Diversity of Fishes: The Largest Group of Extant Vertebrates', a talk given by Byrappa Venkatesh on 23 May 2017 in Singapore as part of the *10-on-10: The Chronicles of Evolution* lecture series. The material here was abstracted and edited by Rebecca Tan.

FURTHER READING

Amemiya et al. (2013) The African coelacanth genome provides insights into tetrapod evolution. *Nature*. 10.1038/nature12027

Brawand et al. (2014) The genomic substrate for adaptive radiation in African cichlid fish. *Nature*. 10.1038/nature13726

Lin et al. (2016) The seahorse genome and the evolution of its specialized morphology. *Nature*. 10.1038/nature20595

Chapter 8

A SALUTE TO OUR PLACODERM PIONEERS

The first time vertebrates had sex

With the help of extremely rare, well-preserved fossils, we can trace complicated sexual behaviours back to ancient armoured fishes called placoderms.

John A. Long

Years before present
10^{10}
10^{9}
10^{8}
10^{7}
10^{6}
10^{5}
10^{4}
10^{3}
10^{2}
10^{1}

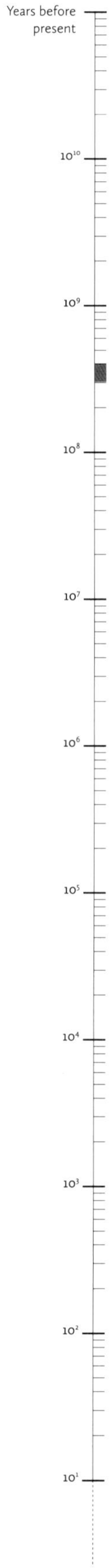

Whether it is the conspicuous and cumbersome tail feathers of a peacock or the boisterous and bloody battles of male elephant seals, sex undoubtedly comes at a cost. Finding a mate can use up a lot of energy and involves taking risks. From an evolutionary point of view, sex is not an efficient way of sharing genes, passing only 50 percent of a parent's genetic material on to the next generation.

> From an evolutionary point of view, sex is not an efficient way of sharing genes, passing only 50 percent of a parent's genetic material on to the next generation.

And yet virtually all multicellular lifeforms do it, from hydrangeas to hamsters and humans. One of the chief advantages of sexual reproduction is that it introduces genetic variation—the all-important substrate of evolution. Because it gives species the opportunity to shuffle the genes of their offspring at every generation, sex helps life on Earth adapt to its ever-changing environment.

STRANGE SEX IN THE SEAS

For the vast majority of all animal species, the benefits of sex so far outweigh the costs that sexual reproduction has almost completely displaced asexual reproduction. But while sexual reproduction itself is now ubiquitous, how each species does it can vary wildly.

For example, most bony fish today reproduce simply by spawning, releasing their sperm and eggs into the water. This type of sex is called external fertilisation as it takes place outside females' bodies. In contrast, more primitive cartilaginous fish like sharks carry out internal fertilisation where males use organs called claspers to place a package of sperm inside the female.

Between these two extremes lies a whole range of bizarre behaviours. Perhaps the strangest of them all are the sex lives of deep-sea anglerfish, where females are about fifty times the size of males. When anglerfish mate, the male becomes attached to the female's head and degenerates into little more than a parasitic bag of sperm. Each female can have more than one male attached to her head at any time, and can draw on them to fertilise her eggs whenever she feels like it.

PAGE 96
Artist's reconstruction of a *Microbrachius* mating scene.

PROGRESS TO CONGRESS

The question I have been trying to address for the past 30 years is when and how complex mating behaviour evolved. After all, for internal fertilisation to happen, male and female fish need to get close enough to become intimate, and stay together long enough for the male to deposit sperm into the female. This is a very complex set of behaviours, requiring the evolution not only of sex-specific hormones but also a radical change in internal anatomy and other modifications.

While observing how modern fish mate can give us an insight into the sheer variety of ways to copulate, it does not reveal what sex was like for the very first creatures to have tried it. For that, we need to turn to the fossil record—the hard data which we can use to reconstruct how life changed over time and diversified into the many species that inhabit the planet today.

Typically, fossils only preserve bones of a prehistoric animal, giving you an idea of its physical shape but shedding no light on how it behaved. Many times, fossilised animals are found crushed or damaged, making even interpretation of the bones difficult. However, in very rare instances, an extremely well-preserved fossil shows up and gives us clear insight into what an animal was doing hundreds of millions of years ago.

In fact, in just the past five or six years, there have been some remarkably important discoveries that have allowed us to trace the origins of complex mating behaviours to primitive fish in a Scottish lake 385 million years ago.

HOW I MET THE MOTHER FISH

It all began with an unusual tangle of tiny bones near the head of a particular specimen we found at the Gogo Formation in the Kimberley region of Western Australia. At first, we couldn't figure out what they were, but it turned out to be the most exciting discovery of my entire career. What we were looking at was actually an embryo, an unborn baby placoderm inside a mother fish—undeniable proof that primitive fish were actually having sex.

Placoderms are an extinct group of armoured fishes that ruled the oceans, rivers and lakes of the world as the dominant vertebrates on Earth for over 70 million years. Once thought to be an evolutionary dead end, they are now recognised as ancestors of us all, developing innovations such as jaws, teeth, paired hind limbs and the first skull with paired plates—effectively 60 percent of the human body plan.

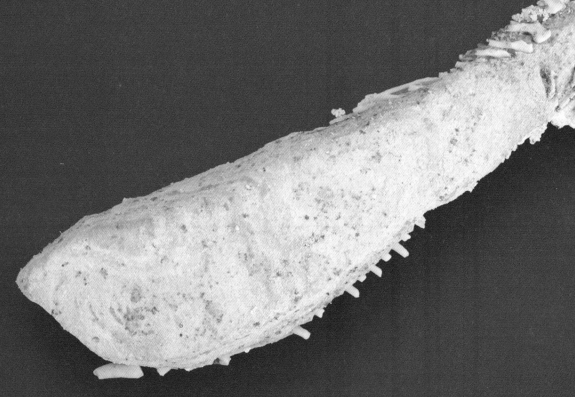

ABOVE
Fossil of a *Materpiscis* body
containing an embryo.
The inset shows the locations
of the embryonic bones,
umbilical cord and yolk sac.

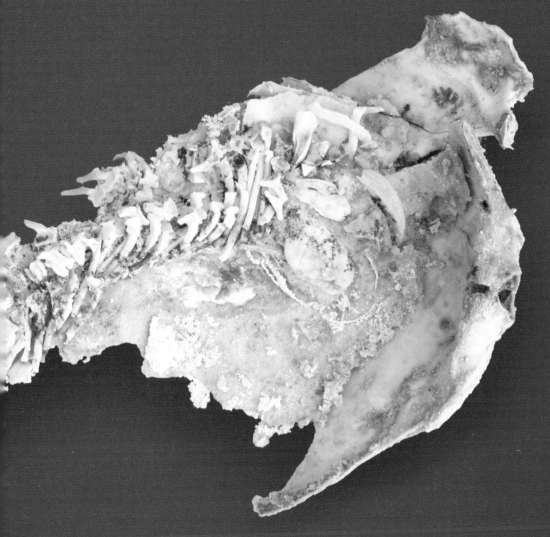

Upper and lower jaws

Embryonic bones

Recrystallised
yolk sac

Umbilical cord

What we were looking at was actually an embryo, an unborn baby placoderm inside a mother fish—undeniable proof that primitive fish were actually having sex.

The fossil we found at Gogo—which we named *Materpiscis attenboroughi* after the English naturalist David Attenborough—belonged to a small group of placoderms called the ptyctodontids. As excited as we were about our discovery, it also raised further questions: Did other more common placoderms also have sex?

There are hundreds of different species of placoderms in a group called the arthrodires, with thousands of specimens in museum collections around the world, making it strange that none of them had ever shown any evidence of embryos like we had seen in the ptyctodontids.

When we revisited those collections, however, we not only found evidence of fossilised embryos, but also an elongated bone called the basipterygium where a male sex organ or clasper could potentially have been attached. The final piece of the puzzle fell into place when my colleague Per Ahlberg at Uppsala University, unencumbered by the notion that placoderm claspers should be attached to the pelvic girdle like those in sharks, identified a clasper fused to the basipterygium.

SOLVING THE MYSTERY OF THE MINI ARMS

But the last and most serendipitous discovery about placoderm sex came in late 2013, when I was in the beautiful medieval walled town of Tallinn in Estonia. While working at the Tallinn University of Technology with the late Elga Mark-Kurik, I was given a shoebox with some bones from a fish belonging to the antiarchs, the most primitive group of placoderms. There I found something truly extraordinary: a clasper with a tube for transferring sperm, on an ancient fish that we didn't even think had pelvic fins.

This finding led me to make two expeditions to the Orkney Islands of northern Scotland where we found well-preserved antiarch samples with intact claspers. For the first time, we also found evidence of female diversity in the form of additional genital plates which probably helped to hold the clasper in position.

The fossils, which we named *Microbrachius dicki* after the Scottish fossil collector Robert Dick, also helped to solve a mystery. *Microbrachius* (which means 'small arms') have crab-like arms with muscles inside a bony shell; these arms were hypothesised to be for walking out of water.

Using three-dimensional printed replicas, we figured out that the arms were for mating, and helped the male and female fish interlock. This makes *M. dicki*'s square-dance-style, side-by-side mating posture the earliest type of mating position in any vertebrate.

BELOW
Artist's reconstruction of *Materpiscis* giving birth.

THE EVOLUTION OF MALE
INTROMITTENT ORGANS

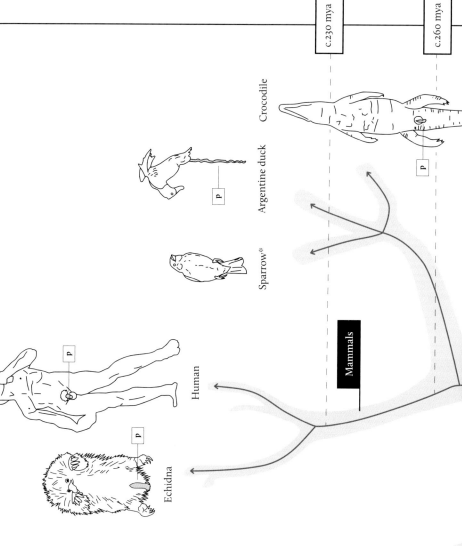

■ Male intromittent organs absent, * secondarily lost

■ Male intromittent organs present

▨ Male intromittent organ types

bcl = bone claspers, independent of pelvic fin

ccl = cartilage claspers developed from pelvic fin

g = gonopodium developed from anal fin

p = penis or paired hemipenes

pf = pelvic fin

c.– mya = approximate divergence time in millions of years

Crocodile

c.230 mya

c.260 mya

Argentine duck

p

Sparrow*

Human

p

Mammals

Echidna

p

Frog*

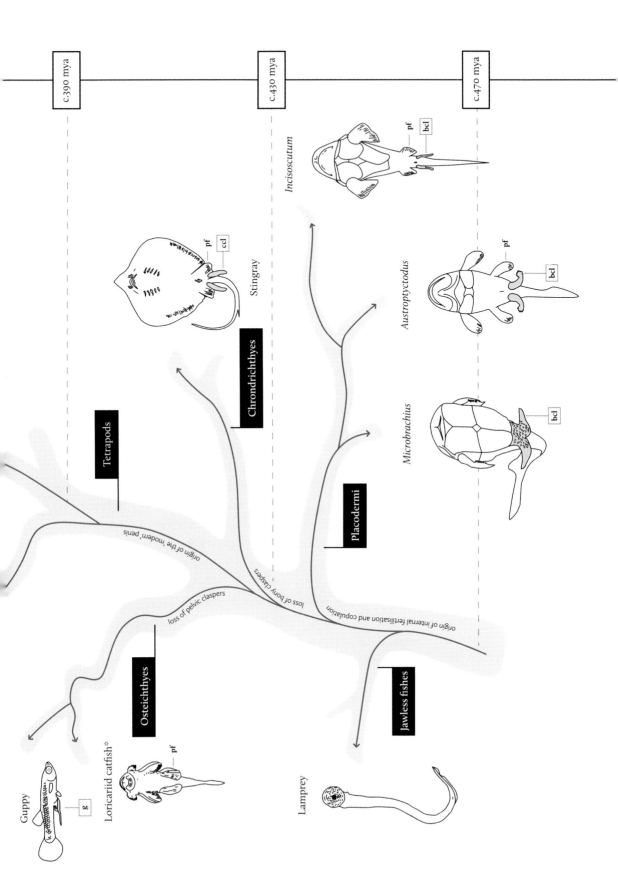

c.390 mya

c.430 mya

c.470 mya

Inciscoscutum

pf

bcl

Stingray

pf

ccl

Austroptyctodus

pf

bcl

Chrondrichthyes

Tetrapods

Microbrachius

bcl

Placodermi

origin of the 'modern' penis

loss of bony claspers

loss of pelvic claspers

origin of internal fertilisation and copulation

Osteichthyes

Jawless fishes

Guppy

g

Loricariid catfish*

pf

Lamprey

......

OF JAWS AND GENITALS

These and other discoveries in the past five years have led to a renaissance in the study of placoderms. To me, the most important fossil found in the past 100 years is a 420-million-year-old placoderm called *Entelognathus primordialis*, found by scientists in the Kuanti formation in Yunnan, China.

E. primordialis is significant because it is the first placoderm with a complex lower jaw to have been found, filling in the biggest gap of evolution: the formation of jaws. Amazingly, all the bones in the jaw of a human being can be traced right back to these bones in the jaws of ancient placoderms.

My own career, however, has focused on another important legacy left to us by the placoderms: our genitals. Developmental biologists have shown that homeobox genes control the formation of limbs, a breakthrough that won Edward B. Lewis, Christiane Nüsslein-Volhard and Eric F. Wieschaus the 1995 Nobel Prize in Physiology or Medicine. More recent findings have identified a specific homeobox gene called *Hoxd13* that not only controls the formation of limbs but also builds claspers in sharks and genital organs in mammals.

These modern-day results from evolutionary developmental biology were a revelation to me as a palaeontologist—here is a gene that connects limbs and genital organs, indicating that placoderm claspers and the mammalian penis probably had a deep and similar evolutionary origin.

The claspers of early jawed fishes were paired to match the development of hind limb bones, and were lost over time as pelvic fins transformed into legs. Instead, other paired reproductive structures such as the hemipenes of reptiles emerged. Eventually, those paired structures became unnecessary, leaving mammals with the single penis that we see today.

So the next time you enjoy the physical pleasures afforded by our modern anatomy, spare a thought for the placoderms which paved the way and pioneered a new—and arguably more fun—way to reproduce.

John A. Long *is the strategic professor in palaeontology at Flinders University in Adelaide, Australia. His research focuses on the early evolution of vertebrates (fishes) as applied to how the human body plan was assembled. He has published over 300 scientific papers and general science articles, and some 28 books. He has named more than 70 new species of prehistoric creatures.*

This chapter is based on 'The Early Evolution of Sex as Told Through the Fossil Record', a talk given by John A. Long on 23 May 2017 in Singapore as part of the *10-on-10: The Chronicles of Evolution* lecture series. The material here was abstracted and edited by Rebecca Tan.

FURTHER READING

Long et al. (2008) Live birth in the Devonian period. *Nature*. 10.1038/nature06966

Long et al. (2009) Devonian arthrodire embryos and the origin of internal fertilization in vertebrates. *Nature*. 10.1038/nature07732

Long (2010) *The rise of fishes: 500 million years of evolution*. Baltimore: Johns Hopkins University Press.

Long (2012) *The dawn of the deed: the prehistoric origins of sex*. Chicago: University of Chicago Press.

Long et al. (2015) Copulation in antiarch placoderms and the origin of gnathostome internal fertilization. *Nature*. 10.1038/nature13825

Chapter 9

WARMING UP
TO MAMMALS

Piecing together the puzzle of mammalian evolution

Chromosomes break and recombine, generating a wealth of genetic diversity that may have been critical for the evolution of mammals.

......

Harris Lewin

Years before present

10^{10}

10^{9}

10^{8}

10^{7}

10^{6}

10^{5}

10^{4}

10^{3}

10^{2}

10^{1}

Looking at a pet cat or dog, it is perhaps difficult to imagine that these mammals are descended from scaly, cold-blooded reptiles. But about 300 million years ago, the first mammal-like reptiles—known as synapsids—appeared, and, over many millennia, evolved some of the defining features of today's mammals. They became warm-blooded, grew hair or fur, gave birth to live young and nursed their offspring with milk from specialised glands.

The closest known relative to modern mammals is *Hadrocodium wui*, a tiny, shrew-like creature that lived some 195 million years ago alongside the dinosaurs of the Jurassic period. Its 12-millimetre-long skull was discovered in 1985 in Yunnan, China, at the Lufeng Basin—a site that has provided many clues about the evolution of land creatures. Being warm-blooded, *Hadrocodium* was able to scuttle around at night and feed on insects while the dinosaurs dozed.

It wasn't until 66 million years ago, after the extinction of the non-bird dinosaurs, that mammals came to rule the day. This marked the start of the Cenozoic era, which extends into the present. Since then, mammals have continued to thrive, increasing in number and diversity. Nearly 6,500 different species of mammals roam the Earth today, and *Homo sapiens*—modern day humans—are counted among them.

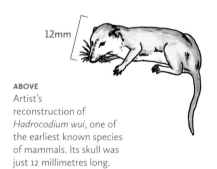

12mm

ABOVE
Artist's reconstruction of *Hadrocodium wui*, one of the earliest known species of mammals. Its skull was just 12 millimetres long.

LEAFING THROUGH THE BOOK OF LIFE

Even as the fossil record continues to inform us about how mammals evolved, scientists have developed new tools in the past five decades that are allowing us to understand evolutionary history with ever greater resolution. Genetic sequencing technology has given us the ability to piece together entire genomes of species, affording us a glimpse, for the first time, of the long thread that ties us to *Hadrocodium*.

Having spent a large part of my research career scrutinising mammalian genomes, I marvel at nature's impressive bookkeeping ability. Contained within each mammalian cell is a record of millions of years of evolution, condensed into microscopic strands of genetic material called chromosomes that collectively make up a genome.

The number of chromosomes varies widely across mammalian species. The Indian muntjac, a deer indigenous to Southeast Asia, has the smallest number of chromosomes known—the males of the species have seven chromosomes, while the females have just six, because the X sex chromosome is fused to autosome 3. On the other end of the spectrum, the red viscacha rat, a rodent native to Argentina, has a whopping 102 chromosomes.

Humans fall somewhere in the middle—we have 46 chromosomes organised into 23 pairs, one pair fewer than our closest living primate cousin, the chimpanzees. But numbers aside, what intrigues me most is the way the genomic information inside chromosomes is arranged, and how this information has changed over time. Collectively, genomes can be viewed as an encyclopaedia of life—they reveal the past, explain the present, and provide clues about the future.

Even though we often regard the genome of a species as an intact volume, it is perhaps more accurately described as an amalgamation of chapters—chromosome segments—that have been duplicated, deleted, fused, split, inverted and translocated throughout the course of life's history. If we take a chromosome-centric view of evolution, the genomes of animal species alive today can therefore be considered the products of successful configurations of chromosomal rearrangements. These rearrangements have become fixed in each species, forming what is known as the species karyotype.

> Collectively, genomes can be viewed as an encyclopaedia of life—they reveal the past, explain the present, and provide clues about the future.

WHEN CHROMOSOMES TAKE A BREAK

Chromosomal rearrangements continue to be a source of genetic variation in animal populations. They occur all the time in nature:

PAGE 108
Circular genome map showing regions of shared gene arrangements between human chromosomes (outermost ring) and (from inner ring outwards) chimpanzee, mouse, rat, dog, chicken and zebrafish chromosomes.

OPPOSITE
Light micrograph
of chromosomes
'crossing over'
during meiosis,
a type of cell
division that
produces sex cells
like sperm and eggs.

when sperm and eggs form through a type of cell division called meiosis, paternal and maternal chromosomes pair up and recombine in a process known as 'crossing over'. In this process, segments of each chromosome break off and get exchanged, but the order and structure of genes on the chromosomes are preserved. The chromosomes that are distributed into the resultant reproductive cells are therefore hybrids of the parental chromosomes.

In some cases, however, rearrangements can disrupt the order or structure of genes on a chromosome. This may result in non-viable offspring or disease—for instance, in patients suffering from a specific subgroup of leukaemia, a segment of chromosome 9 becomes incorrectly fused with chromosome 22, resulting in a novel gene product that drives cancer progression. But not all such disruptive rearrangements are necessarily bad—serendipitous errors do occur, giving rise to beneficial adaptations and, in the long run, new species. It all depends on how the genetic deck is shuffled.

> Chromosomal rearrangements continue to be a source of genetic variation in animal populations.

We used to think that chromosomes break and recombine at random during the course of evolution. This 'random breakage' model was first proposed in the 1980s, and was based on comparisons of the chromosome structures of mice and humans. But as higher-resolution genome sequences emerged for both species, it became apparent that some breakpoint regions were hotspots in chromosomes where the likelihood of breakage was higher than could be expected due to chance alone. These hotspots, also frequently referred to as reuse breakpoints, occur at homologous chromosome regions in different lineages of mammals—unstable sites that appear to have common molecular features.

Intuitively, one might expect that breakpoint regions would be confined to 'gene deserts'—areas of the genome that are devoid of protein-coding genes—where the instability they bring about would presumably wreak less havoc. If a genome were a car, you would rather the windscreen or doors were broken instead of the engine or

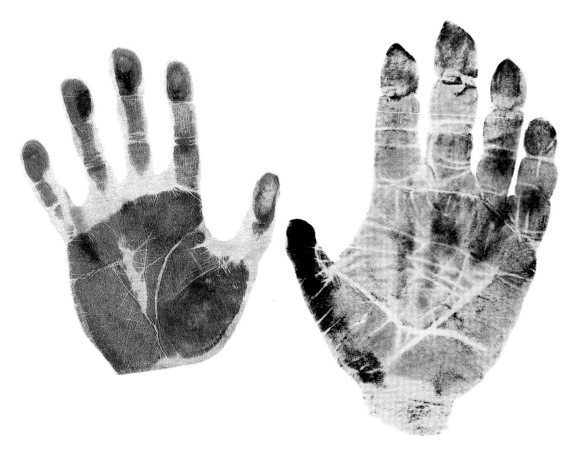

tyres. However, my research has shown that the opposite is true—compared to other parts of a chromosome, breakpoint regions in mammals contain a higher density of genes, including novel genes that control transcription.

Moreover, when we looked at the genomes of nine mammalian species—human, chimpanzee, macaque, pig, cattle, dog, opossum, rat and mouse—we found that genes within breakpoint regions were generally implicated in immunity and muscle function. We think that genomic instability, by creating multiple versions of immune and motor system components, as well as genes controlling other adaptive traits, plays a key role in generating the variation that Darwinian evolution can then act upon. Depending on environmental pressures such as infection and predation, offspring receiving these variants may have a survival advantage. Research in yeast and fruit flies has shown that certain rearrangements are adaptive, and we are doing experiments to determine if the same is true for mammals.

EVOLUTION SHIFTS INTO HIGH GEAR

Given that breakpoint regions are gene-rich and evolutionarily relevant, we can use them to trace the ancestry of mammals. My lab has reconstructed the genomes of seven placental mammals (eutherians) that are ancestors of humans, relying on whole genome assemblies of 19 present-day eutherians, one marsupial (a non-eutherian mammal) and a bird for a distant comparison. Subsequently, using computational methods, we identified a total of 162 chromosomal breakpoints leading to the human lineage that arose over the past 105 million years of mammalian evolution.

The most common chromosomal rearrangements were inversions—when a chromosome fragment breaks off and reinserts itself in reverse orientation. Intriguingly, we observed a high frequency of chromosomal breakpoints in the lineages leading up to rhesus monkeys and chimpanzees, suggesting an accelerated rate of chromosome evolution in primates during the past 43 million years.

Further evidence of acceleration is gleaned from the 9.2 million years separating the ancestor of great apes from the common ancestor of humans and chimpanzees, during which a total of 33 breakpoints occurred—a rate of 3.59 breakpoints per million years. This is in stark contrast to the slower pace of chromosome evolution before the appearance of monkeys and apes—just 0.98 breakpoints per million years.

> When chromosomes break and rearrange, there is not just creation of new gene content, but also new ways of regulating gene expression.

When chromosomes break and rearrange, there is not just creation of new gene content, but also new ways of regulating gene expression. One of our studies, recently submitted for publication, shows this to be the case in mammals. Hence, many of the unique anatomical and physiological adaptations observed in primates and other mammals may have resulted from chromosome rearrangements, in addition to the more classical mutation mechanisms.

......

BUILDING A LIBRARY OF LIFE

Our approach of using information from the genomes of living mammals to reconstruct those of ancestral ones can be applied to other classes of animals to yield insights about their evolutionary pasts. At the same time, with a better understanding of chromosomal rearrangements—where, when and how they occur—we can perform deeper evolutionary analyses to find out which coding or non-coding elements of genomes control the development of adaptive traits.

Returning to the analogy of genomes as books, you might imagine written on their pages the collective wisdom of 3.8 billion years of evolution—the length of time since biological life first appeared on our planet. There is much left to learn about the 1.5 to 2 million species that are known to us, a number that does not include species we have yet to discover. Yet, to date, only 2,500 species have had their genomes sequenced to completion.

> We have proposed a moonshot for biology—to sequence the DNA of all eukaryotic life on Earth over a ten-year period.

This paltry figure is set to change, as the cost of genome sequencing has come down by almost a million-fold in the past two decades. With costs as low as US$1,000 per genome, it is now possible to mount more ambitious expeditions into the 'dark matter of biology'. Thus, a group of scientists, including myself and others at the Smithsonian Institution, the University of Illinois and several other institutions around the world, have proposed a moonshot for biology—to sequence the DNA of all eukaryotic life on Earth over a ten-year period. We call this initiative the Earth BioGenome Project.

What we hope to create is a digital repository of life, which we envision will be used to maximise the returns of science to society, promote human welfare, as well as enable the conservation, protection and restoration of biodiversity. Last but not least, this project promises to reinvigorate our understanding of biology, ecosystems and evolutionary processes, granting us insights that reach further back into the past while simultaneously providing us with a glimpse of possible futures.

Harris Lewin *is vice chancellor for research, distinguished professor of evolution and ecology, and the Robert and Rosabel Osborne Endowed Chair at the University of California, Davis in the US. In the 1990s, his research group was involved in the first comprehensive and detailed mapping of the cattle genome. His research currently focuses on the evolution of mammalian genomes and the role of chromosomal rearrangements in adaptation, speciation and cancer.*

This chapter was contributed by Harris Lewin, and was edited by Jeremy Chan.

FURTHER READING

Murphy et al. (2005) Dynamics of mammalian chromosome evolution inferred from multispecies comparative maps. *Science*. 10.1126/science.1111387

Larkin et al. (2009) Breakpoint regions and homologous synteny blocks in chromosomes have different evolutionary histories. *Genome Research*. 10.1101/gr.086546.108

Kim et al. (2017) Reconstruction and evolutionary history of eutherian chromosomes. *Proceedings of the National Academy of Sciences of the United States of America*. 10.1073/pnas.1702012114

Lewin et al. (2018) Earth BioGenome Project: sequencing life for the future of life. *Proceedings of the National Academy of Sciences of the United States of America*. 10.1073/pnas.1720115115

Chapter 10

ALL IN THE FAMILY

Mapping our evolutionary origins

With a fragmented fossil record and a lack of clear boundaries between species, there is still no clear consensus on the nature of the family tree of *Homo sapiens* and our distant relatives. But new taxonomic approaches now offer researchers better methods for mapping its branches.

Francis Thackeray

Years before present
10^{10}
10^{9}
10^{8}
10^{7}
10^{6}
10^{5}
10^{4}
10^{3}
10^{2}
10^{1}

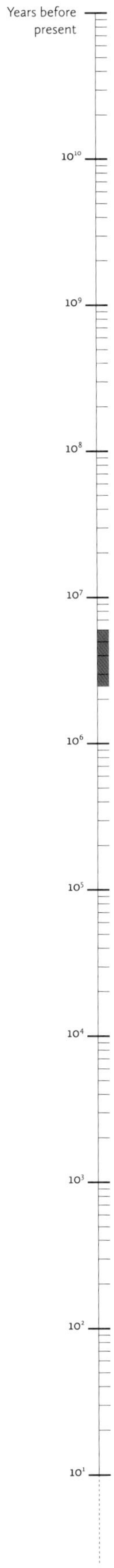

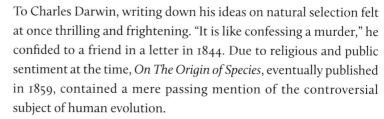

PAGE 118
The Taung Child, unearthed in 1924 in South Africa, became the first known member of the australopithecines, distant ancestors of modern-day humans.

BELOW
Raymond Dart in 1978 with the original Taung Child specimen.

To Charles Darwin, writing down his ideas on natural selection felt at once thrilling and frightening. "It is like confessing a murder," he confided to a friend in a letter in 1844. Due to religious and public sentiment at the time, *On The Origin of Species*, eventually published in 1859, contained a mere passing mention of the controversial subject of human evolution.

By 1871, however, the winds had shifted enough for Darwin to write *The Descent of Man*, in which he argued that humans, too, had evolved through natural selection, just the same as all other species. Further observing that chimpanzees and gorillas—our closest cousins—are found only in Africa, Darwin also proposed that that continent was most likely where early humans had originated.

Today, we have plenty of fossil and genetic evidence to show that Darwin was right. The last common ancestor of humans and apes probably lived some six to seven million years ago in Africa, which scientists now widely recognise as the cradle of humanity.

But this knowledge by no means closes the book on human evolution. With more than 20 hominin species described so far, there is no clear, straight line of descent leading to *Homo sapiens*; instead, our ancestral family tree more closely resembles a bush, bristling with side branches and twigs. The age-old question of "Where did we come from?" thus continues to both fascinate and stymie the field of palaeoanthropology.

DIGGING UP THE PAST

Many important fossils that have helped to make the case for humankind's African origin were discovered in South Africa, the country I hail from and in which I now carry out my research.

In 1924, a fossilised skull unearthed by quarrymen at Taung, South Africa, was described by anatomist Raymond Dart as a new hominin species, one he named *Australopithecus africanus*. The Taung Child, as it came to be called, was the first known member of the australopithecines, a group which comprised multiple species. Our own genus, *Homo*, is thought to have descended from one of these species around 2.5 million years ago.

Another major find was made in 1947, when palaeontologist Robert Broom discovered 'Mrs Ples', a nearly complete *Australopithecus africanus* skull, in the Sterkfontein cave system northwest of Johannesburg. Since these initial discoveries, numerous *Australopithecus*, *Paranthropus*, *Homo* and other hominin fossils have been found at sites in South Africa, Chad, Ethiopia, Kenya, Malawi and Tanzania.

ABOVE
Robert Broom
and Mrs Ples.

This is great news for palaeoanthropologists, who can never have too many fossils to learn from. Yet—somewhat counterintuitively—the ever-increasing number of specimens has perhaps made the picture of human ancestry more, instead of less, bewildering.

WHEN BOUNDARIES BREAK DOWN

To understand why this is the case, let's go back to Darwin for a bit. Before he published *On The Origin of Species*, the man was obsessed with barnacles—for nine years, he dissected, studied and wrote about them on a daily basis.

Darwin noticed that the more specimens of barnacles he looked at, the harder it became to classify them into distinct groups. With that much variability in their morphological features, the boundaries between what he had thought were separate species began to break down.

Today, we see exactly the same thing with hominin fossils. When only a few fossils were known, classifying them was simple.

But the hundreds of specimens now available can no longer be easily pigeonholed into one species or another. Instead, they form a spectrum of variability across evolutionary time and geographical space.

On this spectrum, where does *Australopithecus* end and *Homo* begin? Does a fossil represent a direct ancestor of *Homo sapiens,* or a distant relative from a side branch? Traditional taxonomic approaches, such as alpha taxonomy, attempt to box specimens into distinct categories. But such approaches are inadequate for answering taxonomic questions if they do not quantify the degree to which specimens are related, both within and between species.

OPPOSITE
Mrs Ples, another important specimen of *Australopithecus africanus.*

S IS FOR SIGMA

Our family tree's many branches, overlaps and evolutionary dead ends obstinately defy our penchant for putting things into neat categories. To make sense of our evolutionary past, we need new methods of taxonomy that recognise the fact that clear boundaries between species do not necessarily exist.

Sigma taxonomy, a mathematical approach my colleagues and I are developing, does just that. Sigma, Σ, the Greek counterpart of the letter S, represents the spectrum of variability in organisms across time and space. Instead of assuming that specimens must belong to one category or another, this approach allows us to quantify their relatedness using anatomical measurements.

Imagine that you are looking at two fossil skulls. On one hand, they might be from two different species; on the other, they are just similar enough that you can't be sure. You've made a careful morphometric analysis of the specimens, measuring a host of anatomical features—cranial length, cranial width, orbital breadth, mandible length and so on.

> Our family tree's many branches, overlaps and evolutionary dead ends obstinately defy our penchant for putting things into neat categories.

Now let's put sigma taxonomy to work. We can plot, on a graph, all the measurements from the first fossil against the second, and draw a straight line through them that best fits the data, using a method called linear regression. If the fossils are closely related or from the same species, the data points will fall close to the line, with limited scatter; conversely, if they are distantly related or from different species, the points will fall further away from the line.

By measuring the degree of scatter of the data points around the line, we can quantify the extent to which the two fossils are similar to each other. In other words, we can determine how far apart the fossils lie on the spectrum of variability—a much better alternative to forcing them into rigid, either-or categories.

> Sigma taxonomy allows us to define a species in a way that more accurately reflects the spectrum of variability within a lineage.

THE POWER OF PROBABILITY

This mathematical approach also enables us to come up with a better definition of a species. In the manner described above, my colleagues and I have examined pairs of conspecific (from the same species) individuals, plotted measurements from one against the other, and calculated the degree of scatter between them. We did this for species across more than 70 modern taxa, including mammals such as rodents, ungulates and primates; birds; reptiles; and even invertebrates such as beetles, butterflies and moths.

Across hundreds of these pairwise comparisons, we found something very interesting. Between conspecific individuals, the degree of scatter— as measured by a mathematical term called the standard error of the m-coefficient—has a mean value of -1.61 on a logarithmic scale.

What is the significance of this number? We propose that it approximates a 'biological species constant' (plus or minus a certain degree of variation), essentially providing us with a statistical definition of a species. We can now assess the probability that two specimens are conspecific: if the degree of scatter between them falls within reasonable range of the biological species constant, they likely belong to the same species; if it falls outside that range, they are likely to belong to two different species.

Thus, rather than relying on a fixed set of classification criteria, sigma taxonomy allows us to define a species in a way that more accurately reflects the spectrum of variability within a lineage.

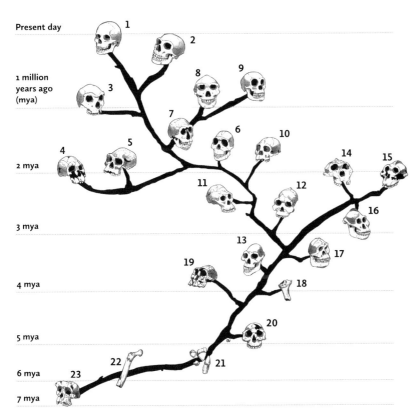

LEFT
A possible history of human evolution, based on sigma taxonomy.

1. *Homo sapiens*
2. *Homo neanderthalensis*
3. *Homo heidelbergensis*
4. *Homo rudolfensis*
5. *Homo habilis*
6. *Homo naledi*
7. *Homo ergaster*
8. *Homo erectus*
9. *Homo floresiensis*
10. *Australopithecus sediba*
11. *Australopithecus africanus*
12. *Australopithecus garhi*
13. *Australopithecus afarensis*
14. *Australopithecus robustus*
15. *Paranthropus boisei*
16. *Paranthropus aethiopicus*
17. *Australopithecus prometheus*
18. *Australopithecus anamensis*
19. *Kenyanthropus platyops*
20. *Ardipithecus ramidus*
21. *Ardipithecus kadabba*
22. *Orrorin tugenensis*
23. *Sahelanthropus tchadensis*

ANALYSING THE FOSSIL RECORD

After testing the concept of a statistical species definition in modern animals, we can now apply it to hominin fossils. If you took the venerable Mrs Ples (the aforementioned fossil of *Australopithecus africanus*) and compared this specimen with skulls attributed to *Homo habilis*, you would expect a degree of scatter indicating that the two are different species. But when we crunched the numbers, what we saw was striking: a value of almost exactly -1.61, suggesting that the skulls are instead members of the same species.

In fact, the two fossils may represent what is termed a chronospecies—organisms from a single lineage that have, over time, changed slightly so that they appear to be morphologically different to some extent. By recognising the spectrum of variability within a lineage, statistical methods allow us to detect connections between members of a chronospecies, when we would otherwise have binned them, erroneously, into separate categories. Sigma taxonomy, therefore, enables us to paint a clearer, more detailed picture of human evolution.

As you read this, fieldwork being undertaken in Africa and elsewhere is turning up still more fossil specimens. In time, these will yield exciting insights into our evolutionary origins. But palaeoanthropology is not just about unearthing and cataloguing new fossils; just as important is the development of new and better approaches for analysing these precious finds. Eventually, such methods will help to bring into focus more leaves, twigs and branches of our human family tree.

> In fact, the two fossils may represent what is termed a chronospecies—organisms from a single lineage that have, over time, changed slightly so that they appear to be morphologically different to some extent.

Francis Thackeray *is a palaeoanthropologist associated with the*
Evolutionary Studies Institute at the University of the Witwatersrand in
Johannesburg, South Africa. His research centres around ancient hominin
fossils from Sterkfontein, Kromdraai, and other caves in the Cradle of
Humankind, a UNESCO World Heritage Site northwest of Johannesburg.
He continues to work on the development of a probabilistic definition of a
biological species.

This chapter is based on 'Human Evolution in Africa, a Probabilistic Definition of a Species and
Sigma Taxonomy', a talk given by Francis Thackeray on 6 June 2017 in Singapore as part of the
10-on-10: The Chronicles of Evolution lecture series. The material here was abstracted and edited
by Shuzhen Sim.

FURTHER READING

Thackeray et al. (1997) Probabilities of conspecificity: application of a morphometric technique to
modern taxa and fossil specimens attributed to *Australopithecus* and *Homo*. *South African Journal
of Science.* 93: 195–96.

Thackeray (2007) Approximation of a biological species constant? *South African Journal of Science.*
103: 489.

Thackeray and Dykes (2016) Morphometric analyses of hominoid crania, probabilities of
conspecificity and an approximation of a biological species constant. *Homo.*
10.1016/j.jchb.2015.09.003

Thackeray and Schrein (2017) A probabilistic definition of a species, fuzzy boundaries and
'sigma taxonomy'. *South African Journal of Science.* 10.17159/sajs.2017/a0206

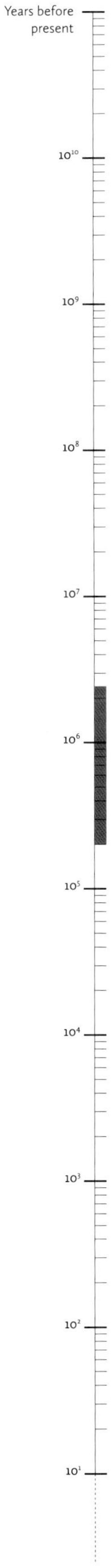

Chapter 11

LESSONS FROM
OUR INNER
NEANDERTHAL

How extinct hominins live on in people today

The genomes of now-extinct archaic humans can help us understand more about what makes modern-day humans truly unique.

Svante Pääbo

Years before present

10^{10}

10^{9}

10^{8}

10^{7}

10^{6}

10^{5}

10^{4}

10^{3}

10^{2}

10^{1}

PAGE 128
Reconstruction of a
Neanderthal man.

Just as old letters, photographs and manuscripts can help historians piece together the past, the human genome—all three billion base pairs of it—offers scientists a vast repository of information with which to reconstruct the genetic history of our species. From this, we know that anatomically modern humans—who were essentially indistinguishable from you and me—evolved in Africa some 100,000 to 200,000 years ago, and subsequently ventured out to colonise the rest of the world.

On their travels, our ancestors would not have found themselves alone. Other forms of humans, having made the same exodus thousands of years earlier, already called parts of the planet home. Most notably, modern humans would encounter the Neanderthals, who lived across large swathes of Western Eurasia until they became extinct some 30,000 years ago.

As the closest evolutionary relatives of present-day humans, Neanderthals are of particular interest to palaeoanthropologists, and indeed have been the focus of my laboratory for the last two decades. By tapping into the rich vein of information within the genomes of present-day and ancient humans, we hope to reconstruct a clearer picture of our biological and anthropological histories, and in so doing, better understand what set modern humans apart from their now-extinct hominin relations.

A fascinating and controversial topic in palaeoanthropology concerns what happened when modern humans and Neanderthals came into contact— specifically, whether or not they interbred.

......

DID THEY OR DIDN'T THEY?

A fascinating and controversial topic in palaeoanthropology concerns what happened when modern humans and Neanderthals came into contact—specifically, whether or not they interbred. Thanks to advances in techniques to sequence ancient DNA, this question, impossible to answer with fossil evidence alone, has now become tractable.

My laboratory has had the wonderful opportunity to sequence DNA from Neanderthal bones found in Vindija Cave, an archaeological site in Croatia. But as you can imagine, working with samples that have weathered the elements for tens of thousands of years is no easy feat. For one, their DNA is a jumble of short fragments that are difficult to sequence and piece together; for another, they are also heavily contaminated with bacteria and fungi. Thus, before we could read the Neanderthal genome, my laboratory first spent years developing new techniques for handling ancient DNA.

Our persistence paid off. In 2010, we published the first 'draft' Neanderthal DNA sequence, which pieced together the genome at a 'coverage' of one-fold, meaning that each base pair had on average been sequenced once; this allowed us to see just over half of the hominin's DNA. Despite its incompleteness, the draft genome still allowed us to address basic questions about the relationship between humans and Neanderthals.

BELOW
A cast of the cranium of the original Neanderthal specimen, which was discovered in the Neander Valley, Germany.

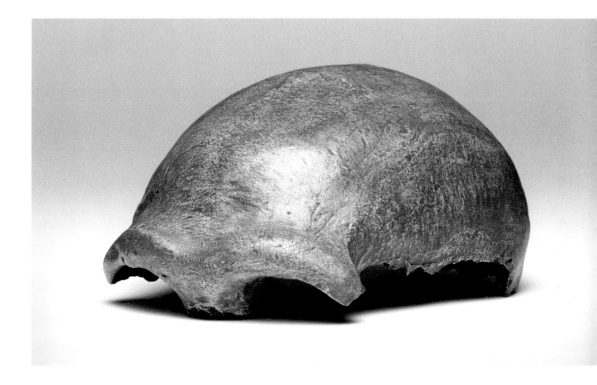

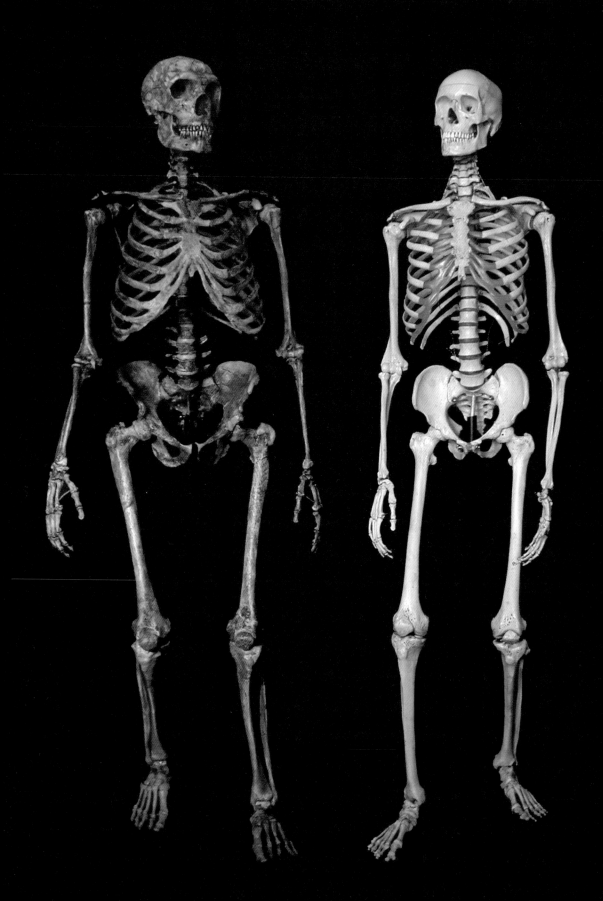

A BRIEF HISTORY OF YOUR GENES

If humans indeed came out of Africa and interbred with Neanderthals in Western Eurasia, we would expect people in Europe to have more in common genetically with Neanderthals than would people in Africa, where Neanderthals have never been. When we compared the Neanderthal genome

If you hail from outside Africa, as much as one to two percent of your own DNA will be of Neanderthal origin.

to those of present-day humans from Europe and Africa, this was exactly what we saw—Neanderthals shared more genetic variants with Europeans than with Africans.

But the plot thickens. Although Neanderthals, as far as we know, never set foot in East Asia or Melanesia, present-day Chinese and Papua New Guinean populations are also genetically closer to Neanderthals than are Africans. What this suggests is that Neanderthals and modern humans started to interbreed even before the ancestors of present-day Europeans, East Asians and Melanesians diverged from one another.

We think that modern humans, on their way out of Africa, first encountered and interbred with Neanderthals in the Middle East. These humans then went on to become the ancestors of everyone outside Africa, such as in East Asia and Melanesia, thus carrying the Neanderthal component of their genomes to the rest of the world. In fact, if you hail from outside Africa, as much as one to two percent of your own DNA will be of Neanderthal origin.

My research group continues to work on laboratory and bioinformatics techniques for coaxing quality DNA sequences out of ancient fossil remains; we have since gone from one-fold coverage of the Neanderthal genome to fifty-fold (in genomics, a high coverage is desirable because it reduces the probability of sequencing errors). From these high-quality sequences, we now know that Neanderthals are not completely extinct—as much as 40 percent of their genome still walks around on two legs, carried in various bits and pieces in the DNA of millions of people around the world.

OPPOSITE
Reconstructed Neanderthal (left) and modern human skeletons.

DISCOVERING THE DENISOVANS

Neanderthal fossils—skulls, teeth and other bones—have been found at hundreds of sites across Europe and Central Asia. By contrast, their relatives the Denisovans are so far known only from two molars and one tiny finger bone—the tip of a pinky—excavated in 2010 at Denisova Cave in Siberia's remote Altai Mountains.

As it turned out, DNA from the finger bone was all we needed to reconstruct a high-quality genome, and thus to identify the Denisovans as a previously unknown form of archaic human. More closely related to Neanderthals than to modern humans, Denisovans were the first new form of extinct humans to be described based on DNA sequence data alone.

With their genome in hand, we can ask the same question about Denisovans as we did about Neanderthals—did they interbreed with modern humans? The answer is yes—people all over mainland Asia harbour small Denisovan DNA contributions of less than one percent; meanwhile, the genomes of people from Papua New Guinea and other parts of Melanesia can be up to five percent Denisovan. Thus, the take-home message is that humans have always interbred with each other.

Because it is unlikely that the ancestors of Melanesians were ever in Siberia, one hypothesis is that they interbred with Denisovans in Southeast Asia before continuing on out into the Pacific. If so, Denisovans may have been more widely spread than their conspicuous absence from the fossil record suggests.

> More closely related to Neanderthals than to modern humans, Denisovans were the first new form of extinct humans to be described based on DNA sequence data alone.

HUMAN BIOLOGY'S DEEP ROOTS

Today, a little of the Neanderthals and Denisovans lives on not only because many of us carry chunks of their DNA, but also

ABOVE
Replica of a tiny finger
bone discovered in
Denisova Cave in
Siberia, Russia.

because their genetic contribution continues to shape aspects of human biology.

In high-altitude Tibet, for example, a large percentage of the population carries a particular version of a gene called *EPAS1*, which, as we now know from careful DNA analysis, came to the ancestors of Tibetans from Denisovans. By allowing for better oxygen transport without increasing blood haemoglobin levels, this gene variant is thought to enable Tibetans to live on the 'roof of the world' without running an increased risk of blood clots and strokes. Thus, if not for a trait acquired tens of thousands of years ago through interbreeding with another form of human, the Tibetan Plateau might be a much more desolate place than it is today.

But some traits acquired from our ancient hominin relatives are less desirous—a Neanderthal version of the *SLC16A11* lipid transporter gene, for example, turns out to increase the risk of type 2 diabetes in Asian and Native American populations. For a Neanderthal dealing with a scarce food supply, this gene variant might well have been an advantageous metabolic adaptation to fend off starvation; only recently, in the context of our modern lifestyles, has it become detrimental.

......

SETTING OURSELVES APART

Intriguingly, Neanderthals, Denisovans and present-day humans—but not apes—also share a variant of *FOXP2*, a gene known to be crucially important for humans to produce and understand speech. While the presence of this variant doesn't necessarily mean that Neanderthals and Denisovans talked the way we do, an understanding of what it does could potentially speak volumes about the origins of our unique capacity for language.

Although mice cannot speak, they remain a useful animal model for studying gene function. When we introduced the human version of *FOXP2* into laboratory mice, they turned out, in maze navigation experiments, to be better at motor learning than normal animals; in addition, they developed neurons with longer extensions in the cortico-basal ganglia, a brain region involved in motor learning. Based on these experiments, we think that the human *FOXP2* variant allows for better proceduralisation, or automation, of motor activity—the same mechanism that kicks in when you finally learn to ride a bicycle after failing several times.

What does this have to do with language? One could argue that articulate speech is the most sophisticated motor activity that humans perform, involving millisecond control and coordination between the vocal chords, tongue and lips. There is still a lot to be learned about how *FOXP2* coordinates these actions, and we and others continue to use animal and other laboratory models to explore its role.

While variants in genes like *FOXP2* may differentiate humans, Neanderthals and Denisovans from apes, we are also deeply interested in what sets present-day humans apart even from our closest, now-extinct hominin relatives. By studying gene variants that were *not* contributed to us by Neanderthals or Denisovans, we hope to identify traits that have played a role in making us—the only species on the planet with complex language, culture, technology and art—uniquely human.

Svante Pääbo *is a director at the Max Planck Institute for Evolutionary Anthropology in Leipzig, Germany. His laboratory has developed techniques for sequencing ancient DNA, which they have used to determine high-quality Neanderthal genome sequences, as well as to discover the Denisovans, a previously unknown hominin group. Pääbo's work allows for the reconstruction of the recent evolutionary history of our species, leading to the realisation that Neanderthals contributed DNA to present-day humans living outside of Africa.*

This chapter is based on 'A Neanderthal View of Modern Human Origins', a talk given by Svante Pääbo on 6 June 2017 in Singapore as part of the *10-on-10: The Chronicles of Evolution* lecture series. The material here was abstracted and edited by Shuzhen Sim.

....

FURTHER READING

Green et al. (2010) A draft sequence of the Neandertal genome. *Science*. 10.1126/science.1188021

Meyer et al. (2012) A high-coverage genome sequence from an archaic Denisovan individual. *Science*. 10.1126/science.1224344

Prüfer et al. (2014) The complete genome sequence of a Neandertal from the Altai Mountains. *Nature*. 10.1038/nature12886

Sankararaman et al. (2014) The landscape of Neandertal ancestry in present-day humans. *Nature*. 10.1038/nature12961

Pääbo (2014) *Neanderthal man: in search of lost genomes.* New York: Basic Books.

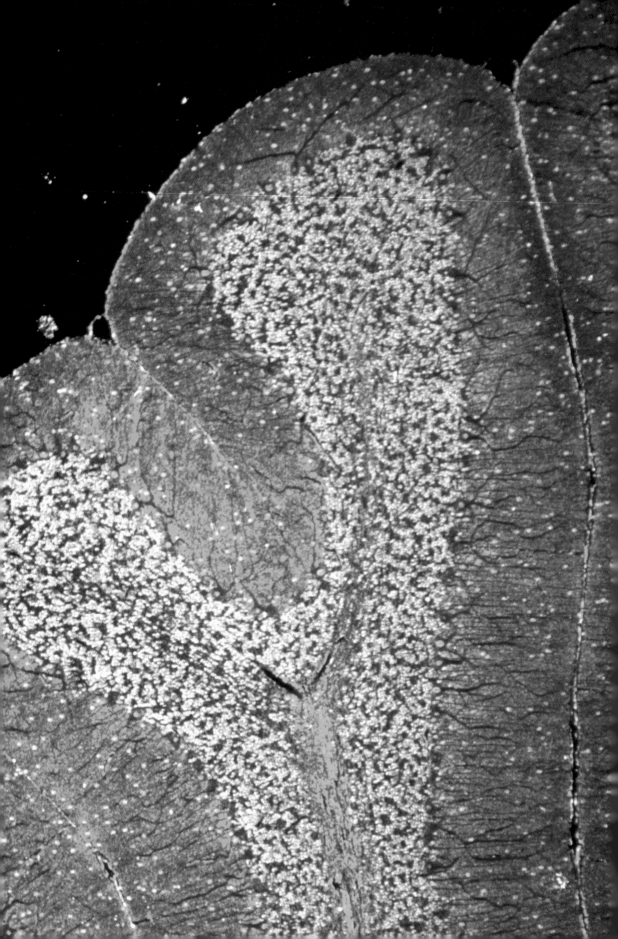

Chapter 12

10^{10}

10^9

10^8

WIRED FOR

10^7

INTELLIGENCE

10^6

10^5

How big brains came to be

Widely regarded as the crowning glory of our species, the human
brain is an extremely complicated organ, and the story of its origins
highlights some of the most important principles of evolution.

10^4

10^3

Terrence Sejnowski

10^2

10^1

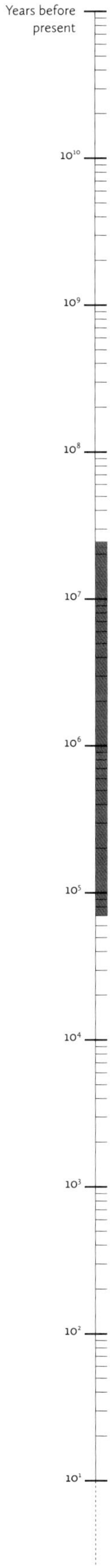

At a meagre two percent of our body weight, the human brain commands 20 percent of the body's blood flow and 20 percent of its energy.

Gaze into the eyes of our closest living primate cousins, the chimpanzees, and one might glimpse a familiar intelligence—not the raging bonfire of human intellect, but perhaps, a spark that never took to kindling.

Six million years separate our species, *Homo sapiens*, from the great apes. During that blink in evolutionary time, the human brain tripled in size, whereas the brains of apes remained relatively unchanged. Other hominins of our ancestral lineage—the Neanderthals and the Denisovans—rivalled modern humans in their cranial capacity, but they became extinct tens of thousands of years ago, leaving us as the most cerebral of apes.

At a meagre two percent of our body weight, the human brain commands 20 percent of the body's blood flow and 20 percent of its energy. Indeed, the constraints of nutrients and energy probably imposed an upper limit on the size of such a metabolically demanding organ.

Nonetheless, the human brain is one of the most complex devices in the known universe, and I have spent most of my career trying to understand its origins and how it functions. But even the most impressive of constructs has humble beginnings, and going back in evolutionary time, we can trace the steps that have gradually led to the appearance of big brains.

......

PUTTING THE 'ION' IN EVOLUTION

If you look at the different levels of organisation of the brain, from the entire central nervous system all the way down to the molecules responsible for the brain's electrical and chemical activity, you will see that there are ten orders of spatial scale. The events occurring at the smallest scale form the basis of all other higher brain functions, so to explain how the brain came about, we must first understand how neurons became capable of firing impulses.

A nerve impulse is fundamentally the exchange of ions across a biological membrane. But because biological membranes are made of lipids, ions—which carry charges—cannot pass through them, except in areas where ion channels are present. These ion channels form pores in the membrane, like gates in a fence, allowing ions to enter and exit the neuron.

Far from being a novel invention, ion channels can be found even in the most primitive single-celled organisms, such as bacteria, which have existed for more than three billion years. These microbes possess potassium ion channels consisting of two transmembrane regions that 'puncture' the membrane and grant passage to potassium ions, as well as other ion channels containing six transmembrane regions that respond to voltage differences.

But the fascinating thing is this: the same six-transmembrane structure, and the gene that codes for it, has been repeatedly duplicated, adapted and expanded upon over evolutionary time to give rise to a host of other ion channels—some with 12 and 24 transmembrane regions, for example. These allowed not only potassium ions, but also sodium and calcium ions to flow in and out of cells, multiplying the capacity for electrical conductance in biological systems.

Herein lies an important principle in evolution—a useful gene is conserved and duplicated, creating a new gene product that becomes specialised for a particular function. A human neuron carries dozens of different types of ion channels distributed along its length, each type a descendant of the ion channel first formed in bacteria.

PAGE 138
Light micrograph of a cross-section through the cerebellum of the brain, which is responsible for motor control and cognitive functions in humans.

BRIDGING BRAIN CELLS

But the firing of electrical impulses in individual neurons does not a brain make. The very metaphor used to describe the event—firing—alludes to a payload and a target, reflecting how one neuron sends a signal to the next: by sending a payload of molecules, known as neurotransmitters, to a target neuron.

Herein lies an important principle in evolution—a useful gene is conserved and duplicated, creating a new gene product that becomes specialised for a particular function.

————————————

When an electrical impulse reaches the 'sending' end of a neuron, called the axon, an influx of calcium triggers the expulsion of tiny packets of neurotransmitters into the external environment. These neurotransmitters bind to receptors on a receiver neuron, relaying a signal to it by modifying the flow of charges across it.

All the parts involved in this transmission process constitute a structure known as the synapse—my favourite structure in the brain. By some estimates, there are a thousand trillion synapses in the human brain—an astronomical number! Mammalian synapses are very complex, consisting of numerous molecular 'nuts and bolts' that package, release and receive neurotransmitters.

Yet, even the mammalian synapse is not an original assembly. The earliest synaptic machinery is found in yeast, although in these single-celled organisms, the so-called protosynapse was used for sensing the environment rather than for sending electrical impulses between cells.

Similar to ion channels, the genes encoding the protosynapse underwent expansion and became specialised for new functions over time. Scientists have sequenced the genomes of sponges, considered the earliest and simplest of animals, and found that these aquatic creatures had already evolved the machinery to carry out calcium signalling and traffic molecular cargo between cells—the essential components of a synapse. The seeds for synaptogenesis thus took root as early as a billion years ago.

OPPOSITE
Light micrograph of synapses between a motor neuron and muscle cells. Motor neurons can activate or inhibit muscle activity.

......

CONFIGURED FOR COGNITION

With ion channels and the basic elements of the synapse arising along the tree of life, the next significant step in the evolution of

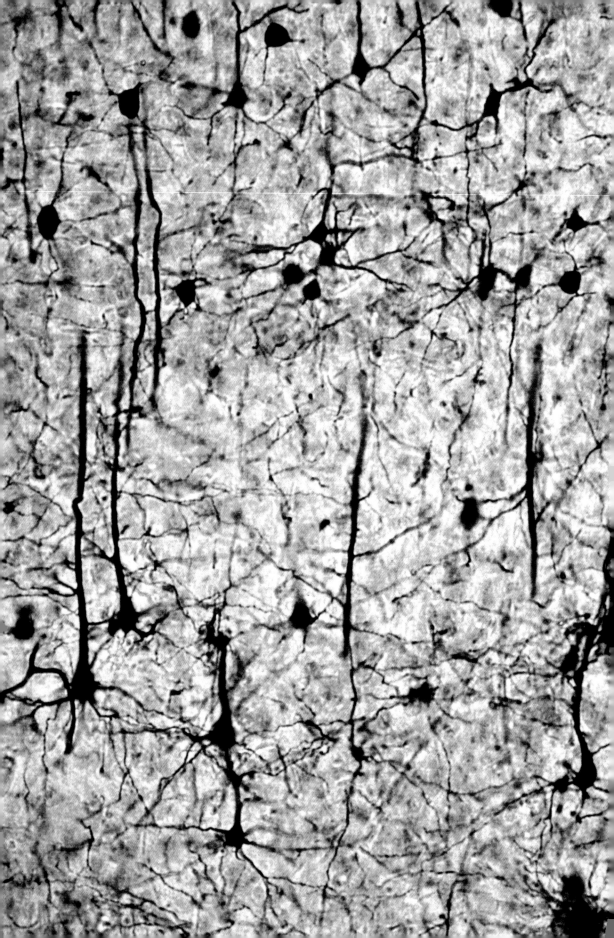

the brain was finding the right configuration for these functional modules. One such successful configuration—the nerve net—appeared approximately 600 million years ago.

Cnidarians, a group of animals that includes corals and jellyfish, were the first to possess nerve nets—diffuse nervous systems wherein neurons are interspersed among the epithelial layers of the organism. Within these nerve nets, we begin to see specialisation of neurons and their clustering into ganglia. These adaptations enabled multiple tiers of organisation of neuronal circuits, thus making room for much greater complexity in their design.

Even when nerve nets were in fashion, other neuronal innovations continued to manifest. A quicker way to propagate signals within neurons was achieved through myelination, which is the coating of axons in a fatty sheath. This faster wiring became the preferred mode of transmission of nerve impulses among placoderms—primitive fish that were the earliest ancestors of vertebrates. In addition, the placoderms developed skulls to encase and protect their myelinated central nervous systems. Armed with what might have been the sharpest weapon of their time, placoderms dominated the seas 400 million years ago.

But as developed as fish brains were, amphibians and reptiles were the first animals to develop a complex forebrain, or cortex, comprising three layers. This architecture persists in the hippocampus and the olfactory cortex of the mammalian brain, enabling long-term memory and the processing of odours. In this, we once again see how useful implements are retained and refined over evolutionary time.

OPPOSITE
Light micrograph of pyramidal neurons in the human cerebral cortex. Pyramidal neurons are a major class of excitatory neurons in the mammalian cerebral cortex, and are important for many cognitive processes.

OF METHYLOMES, MICE AND MEN

Arguably, the most important invention to have arisen during the 150-million-year interval between reptiles and mammals was the evolution of the six-layer mammalian neocortex. Along with this doubling of layers came still more specialisation—even today, we do

EVOLUTION OF THE NERVOUS SYSTEM

1 m	10 cm	1 cm	1 mm	100 μm	1 μm	1 Å
CNS	Systems	Maps	Networks	Neurons	Synapses	Molecules

TOP
The nervous system encompasses ten orders of magnitude of spatial scale, ranging from the entire central nervous system (CNS) all the way down to neurotransmitter molecules.

RIGHT
From rudimentary ion channels in bacteria and nerve nets in cnidarians, the nervous system evolved over billions of years to the six-layer cortex seen today in mammals.

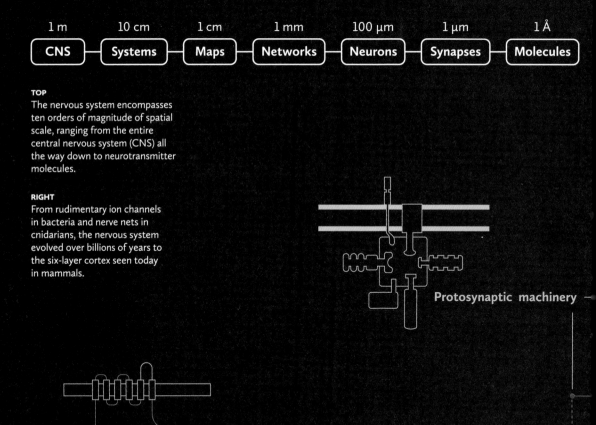

Protosynaptic machinery

Ion channels

| 3000 | 2800 | 2600 | 2400 | 2200 | 2000 | 1800 | 1600 |

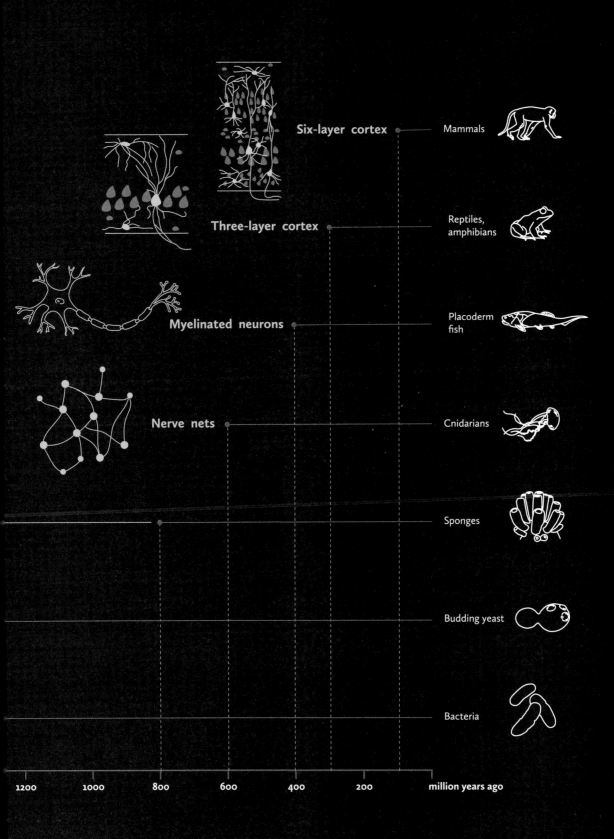

Six-layer cortex ⎯⎯ Mammals

Three-layer cortex ⎯⎯ Reptiles, amphibians

Myelinated neurons ⎯⎯ Placoderm fish

Nerve nets ⎯⎯ Cnidarians

Sponges

Budding yeast

Bacteria

1200   1000   800   600   400   200   million years ago

not actually know how many different types of neurons there are in the mammalian brain.

My lab is particularly interested in trying to answer this question. We are defining the different types of neurons in the mammalian cortex by their DNA methylation patterns, or methylomes. Methylation refers to small molecular tags attached to DNA which modify gene expression. DNA contains four different types of nucleic acids identified by four letters—A, C, G and T—and methylation occurs on Cs that sit beside Gs, known as methylated CG or mCG sites.

However, of all the organs, the brain is the only one that has mature cells where a substantial fraction of methylation occurs on Cs sitting next to As, Cs or Ts. We call these mCH sites, where H can represent an A, C or T. In human neurons, 53 percent of all possible CH sites are methylated. This unique feature must have some special function, especially given how the methylation pattern changes in tandem with the formation of synapses during neural development.

We have also examined the methylomes of neurons in mouse and human brains and found that they correspond not only to particular cell types, but also to the locations of these cell types within the six layers of the mammalian neocortex. Intriguingly, it looks as if humans have a couple of new neuron types that are not found in mice.

Hence, by comparing the genetics, methylation patterns, structures and functions of human brains with those of other organisms, we can piece together in greater detail how the crowning glory of *Homo sapiens* came to be, and how it enabled language, culture and technology. With this knowledge, we may perhaps chart the path towards the future, especially in the domain of machine learning. After all, our intelligence was sculpted over millennia by evolution; thus, nature's "endless forms most beautiful"—as Darwin termed life on Earth—should prove to be a rich source of inspiration for the creation of artificial intelligence.

> Our intelligence was sculpted over millennia by evolution; thus, nature's "endless forms most beautiful"—as Darwin termed life on Earth—should prove to be a rich source of inspiration for the creation of artificial intelligence.

Terrence Sejnowski *is an investigator with the Howard Hughes Medical Institute and a distinguished professor at the University of California, San Diego in the US; he also holds the Francis Crick Chair at the Salk Institute for Biological Studies. His research combines experimental and computational neuroscience to better understand brain functions and how they give rise to complex behaviours.*

This chapter is based on 'Evolving Brains', a talk given by Terrence Sejnowski on 14 July 2017 in Singapore as part of the *10-on-10: The Chronicles of Evolution* lecture series. The material here was abstracted and edited by Jeremy Chan.

FURTHER READING

Allman (1999) *Evolving brains*. New York: Scientific American Library.

Laughlin and Sejnowski (2003) Communication in neuronal networks. *Science*. 10.1126/science.1089662

Roth et al. (2013) Evolution of nervous systems and brains. In: *Neurosciences—from molecule to behavior: a university textbook* (eds. Galizia and Lledo). Berlin: Springer Spektrum.

Luo (2015) *Principles of neurobiology*. New York: Garland Science.

Luo et al. (2017) Single-cell methylomes identify neuronal subtypes and regulatory elements in mammalian cortex. *Science*. 10.1126/science.aan3351

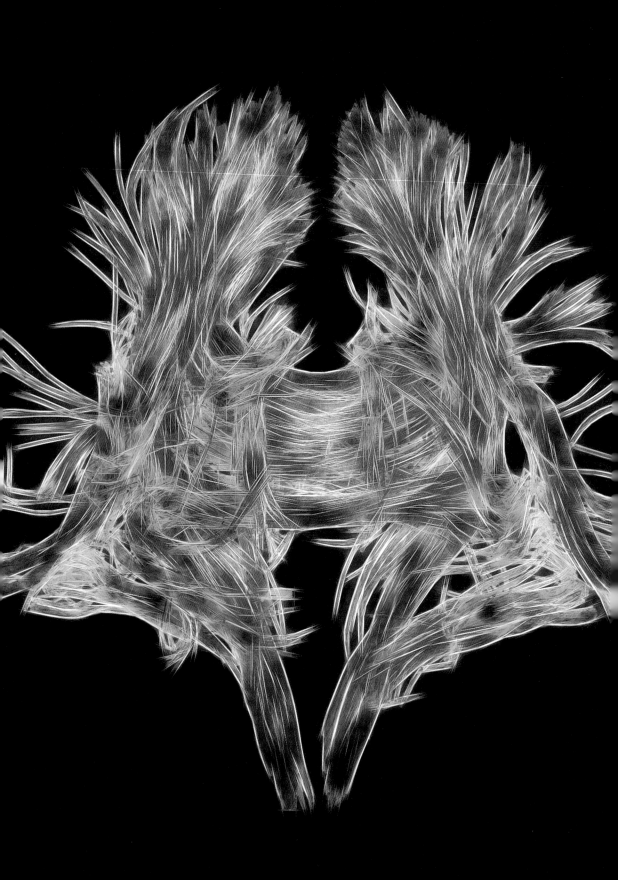

Chapter 13

Years before
present

10^{10}

10^9

10^8

GETTING SMART
ABOUT
LEARNING

10^7

10^6

10^5

The ascendance of human intelligence

By picking the brains of non-human primates, we can uncover
clues about how *Homo sapiens* came to acquire its impressive
capacity for learning.

10^4

10^3

Atsushi Iriki

10^2

10^1

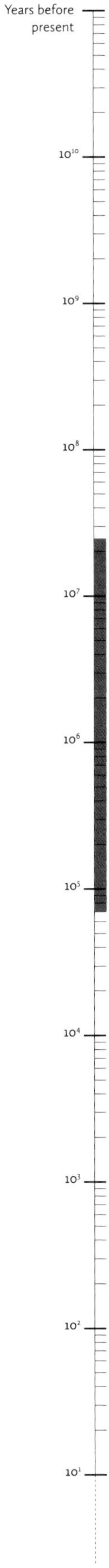

The human infant has often been described as a blank slate. Yet, an underlying assumption of this description is a newborn's remarkable ability to learn. From manipulating objects and producing speech to the reading and writing of text, the human child is inherently capable of acquiring complex knowledge and skills throughout his or her lifetime.

Compared to other species, *Homo sapiens'* capacity for learning seems significantly expanded. We intuitively think that our larger brains make us more intelligent, and indeed, the human brain is disproportionately large for mammals our size.

But pure observation of brain size and anatomy yields a static picture that cannot fully account for how brains process information and produce adaptive behaviours—the fundamental inputs and outputs of learning. Also incomplete is the knowledge gleaned from the fossil record; brains, being soft tissue, do not weather well the ravages of time.

> We intuitively think that our larger brains make us more intelligent, and indeed, the human brain is disproportionately large for mammals our size.

How then can we create testable hypotheses to better understand the evolutionary basis of learning? This has been my research interest for almost three decades. By studying the non-human primate brain, I have attempted to explain the evolutionary mechanisms that enable learning and describe how our brains continue to co-evolve with the environments we create.

A MALLEABLE MACHINE

When a piece of dough is prodded and pulled, it yields to the force and changes shape. A similar reaction, albeit on the microscopic scale, is triggered in the brain during learning. Although early studies depicted the brain as a fixed and rigid entity throughout adulthood, more recent data has shown that the brain constantly reorganises itself in response to environmental cues. This feature is known as plasticity.

At the same time, we know that biological systems rarely operate at full efficiency. If a system is overly specialised, it becomes unwieldy in the event of unexpected challenges. Thus, the brain has some degree of redundancy built in—specific brain regions are adapted for performing particular tasks, but there is some spare capacity within each region to take on new functions.

Collectively, these biological principles give the brain an unprecedented level of adaptability and may help explain how the primate brain gradually evolved into the human brain. Through the slow expansion of neural capacity under environmental selection, new 'pockets' of specialised brain regions—what I call neural niches— could have formed, which in turn gave rise to new functions, or cognitive niches.

And so, around 25 years ago, I began to explore whether new neural and cognitive niches could spontaneously appear in the monkey brain. But instead of looking naively into the monkey brain, I trained monkeys to use different tools and probed for changes in the structure and function of their brains.

PAGE 150
Magnetic resonance imaging scan of bundles of white matter nerve fibres in the brain, which relay information between different brain regions.

A MATTER OF GREY MATTER

Take a small step backwards in primate evolutionary history—just 25 million years—and you will find the last common ancestor of apes and monkeys. While apes such as chimpanzees and gorillas demonstrate a propensity to use tools, this inclination is very rare in monkeys, a group which includes macaques and baboons. Nonetheless, the sparse anecdotal evidence of monkeys wielding twigs and stones in the wild suggests that the potential to use tools already exists in the monkey brain.

In my lab, monkeys were first given a rake to retrieve food that was out of their reach. After 10 to 14 days of training, they became proficient in this task. Interestingly, as the monkeys' skill with the

rake improved, their brains no longer distinguished where the arm ended and where the rake began. We sometimes say that a skilful person 'becomes one' with the instrument of his or her trade. This was literally what I saw happening with the monkeys.

Moreover, the monkey's brain tracked the rake like part of its body, much like how we retain a sense of where each part of our body is even with our eyes closed. But what surprised me most was my observation that the cortical grey matter of the monkey brain had increased by up to 23 percent after training. To accommodate the rake, the monkey had unwittingly created a new space—a new neural niche—in its brain dedicated to tool use.

Could more of such neural niches arise with other kinds of tools? This was what I set out to discover next.

OPPOSITE
Monkeys like the Japanese macaque may develop new neural niches when learning how to use tools.

A HIERARCHY OF ACQUIRED ABILITIES

Tools can be classified into different categories: motor tools such as the rake extend our physical functions, while tools such as a camera extend our senses. Clearly, a camera is more sophisticated than a rake, and I wanted to know if monkeys could learn to use this 'higher-order' tool.

To test this, I provided untrained monkeys with a kind of endoscope—a camera mounted at the end of a stick. The monkeys were supposed to use the endoscope to locate food outside their field of vision and beyond their reach. I thought this would be easy for the monkeys, but I was wrong. For years, I was unable to get the monkeys to use the endoscope.

> To accommodate the rake, the monkey had unwittingly created a new space—a new neural niche—in its brain dedicated to tool use.

The breakthrough only came when I started experiments with monkeys that had already been trained to use the rake. To my surprise, mastery of the rake seemed to unlock the monkeys' ability to comprehend the rules associated with images from a mirror attached to the tip of the rake. This set them on the path towards being able to use the endoscope—step by step, they eventually learnt to use it to seek out hidden food. There is thus a hierarchy to learning and intelligence—the monkey's initial development of the motor skill served as a gateway to its ability to recognise and interpret images from the endoscope.

In both humans and monkeys, the parietal cortex of the brain is responsible for motor control, such as waving an arm, and spatial processing, such as catching a ball in mid-air. However, the parietal cortex in humans is flanked by numerous brain regions not found in monkeys, suggesting that outgrowths of the parietal cortex eventually gave rise to new neural niches and functions.

It is perhaps no coincidence, then, that the way we think and communicate is steeped in spatial undertones. In many languages or cultures, when we say 'the secret *behind* it' or 'something *under* the table', the logical structure is built on spatial information principles.

A RITE OF INHERITANCE

We now know that monkeys can construct new specialised brain regions (neural niches) to fulfil novel functions (cognitive niches) and that these changes happen within their lifetimes. But if advantageous learned behaviours, such as tool use, are not inherited by offspring, then evolution cannot be said to have occurred.

Here is where the Baldwin effect provides a helpful explanation. Named after American philosopher and psychologist James Mark Baldwin, the Baldwin effect proposes that natural selection favours individuals that are flexible in their behaviour. This flexibility makes them more capable of surviving new challenges, such as drastic changes to their habitats.

As a result of this behavioural plasticity, genes and mutations that would otherwise have been neutral (neither beneficial nor detrimental) end up gaining some form of context-specific utility,

and get passed down to the next generation. Given time, a specific configuration of these genes and mutations becomes stabilised as the de facto genotype for enhanced learning ability.

The Baldwin effect, at its core, still adopts a Darwinian, outside-in approach to explain the evolution of learning. The environment, or ecological niche, provides the selection pressure to alter the neural and cognitive niches. Having said this, the pace at which learning evolved in humans seems unreasonably rapid for a process subjected to natural selection alone.

ABOVE
Monkeys that have already mastered simpler motor skills can later learn to use higher-order tools, according to the author's research.

......

THE INTERMINGLING OF NICHES

Even as the human brain was moulded by the environment, the environment was also inevitably shaped by human activity. Arguably, natural selection underestimates this inverse effect of human selection on the environment.

The three niches—ecological, neural and cognitive—should therefore be viewed as interacting in a cyclical rather than linear fashion. Each time a new brain region (neural niche) and function (cognitive niche) came about, it allowed our species to make ever greater changes to our environment (ecological niche), which in turn triggered more changes in the human brain. The continuous building up of all three niches is what I call triadic niche construction.

In many ways, triadic niche construction helps explain the onset of the era that geologists call the Anthropocene—adapted from the Greek word *ánthrōpos*, for 'human being'. This is an apt term because human activity now determines the state of the Earth. Never before in the course of evolutionary history has a single species had such an outsized influence on the global ecosystem.

> Novel neural and cognitive niches can allow us to explore and exploit even abstract or conceptual spaces, such as values and morals.

Yet, the Earth's resources are finite, and as exploitation of our ecological niche approaches physical limits, does this also signal an end to the growth of our neural and cognitive niches? I, for one, am optimistic that the evolution of our learning capacities will continue, because the idea of niche construction is not restricted to physical space.

Novel neural and cognitive niches can allow us to explore and exploit even abstract or conceptual spaces, such as values and morals, which overlay physical space, like pieces of paper stacking into a new dimension. Thus, without abandoning the biological reality and primate origins of niche constructions, we will be able to sustain our growth as a species long into the future.

Atsushi Iriki *is head of the laboratory for symbolic cognitive development at the RIKEN Brain Science Institute in Japan, and concurrently serves as president and CEO of RIKÆNALYSIS Corporation. His research focus is on neurobiological mechanisms explaining the evolutionary precursors of human higher cognitive functions.*

This chapter is based on 'A Presage of Anthropocene: How the Primate Brain and Its Learning Capacity Co-evolves with the Environment', a talk given by Atsushi Iriki on 14 July 2017 in Singapore as part of the *10-on-10: The Chronicles of Evolution* lecture series. The material here was abstracted and edited by Jeremy Chan.

FURTHER READING

Iriki and Sakura (2008) The neuroscience of primate intellectual evolution: natural selection and passive and intentional niche construction. *Philosophical Transactions of the Royal Society B: Biological Sciences*. 10.1098/rstb.2008.2274

Quallo et al. (2009) Gray and white matter changes associated with tool-use learning in macaque monkeys. *Proceedings of the National Academy of Sciences of the United States of America*. 10.1073/pnas.0909751106

Iriki and Taoka (2012) Triadic (ecological, neural, cognitive) niche construction: a scenario of human brain evolution extrapolating tool use and language from the control of reaching actions. *Philosophical Transactions of the Royal Society B: Biological Sciences*. 10.1098/rstb.2011.0190

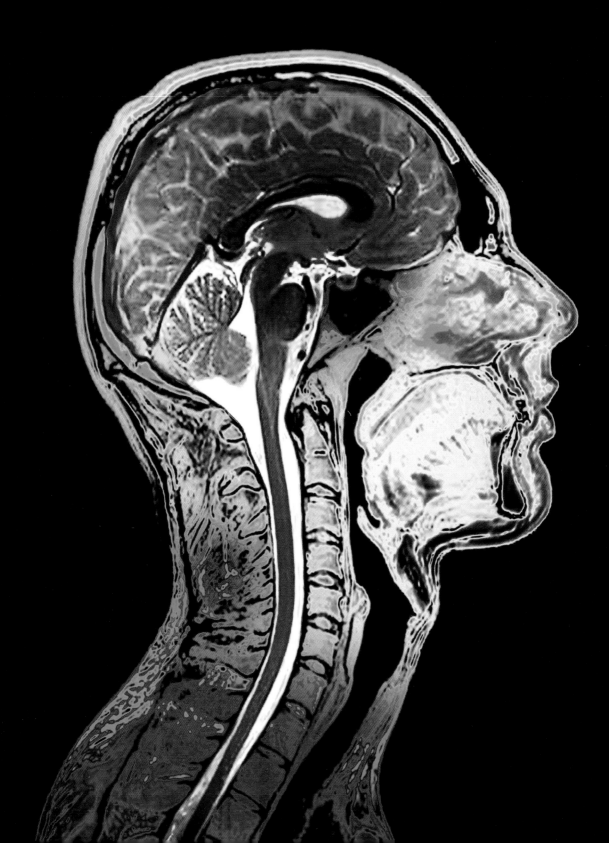

Chapter 14

10^{10}

10^{9}

10^{8}

MORE THAN JUST
SMALL TALK

10^{7}

10^{6}

Seeking the roots of human language
within the tree of life

10^{5}

Human language leaves behind no fossil record, but scientists
can use comparative biology and genetics to piece together the
evolutionary origins of our gift of speech.

10^{4}

10^{3}

Tecumseh Fitch

10^{2}

10^{1}

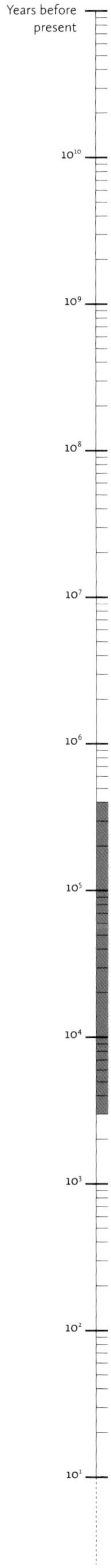

Within a year of birth, the human infant begins to babble sounds that approximate simple words. Parents everywhere hail this as a significant milestone and appear visibly impressed, despite the fact that language acquisition is very much a part of every child's normal development. But perhaps such a reaction is warranted—the faculty of language is what sets us apart from all other species in the animal kingdom.

All animals communicate, be it with birdsong, whistles or growls. But none of these communication systems approaches the boundless expressivity that human language encompasses. Our ability to bring together discrete sounds to invent an infinite variety of meanings makes us truly unique.

How human language evolved has been a subject of keen interest in the scientific disciplines of anthropology, linguistics, neurobiology and psychology. The diversity of hypotheses presented in the scholarly literature attests to how difficult it is to pinpoint the origins of this defining trait of *Homo sapiens*. Because languages and linguistic behaviour do not fossilise, any evidence we find will be indirect and open to interpretation.

> Our ability to bring together discrete sounds to invent an infinite variety of meanings makes us truly unique.

Even so, this does not mean that the evolution of language is a black box never to be demystified. By taking a broadly comparative approach—that is, studying a wide variety of species and noting their biological similarities and differences—we can formulate testable hypotheses about specific aspects of language, and hence piece together the bigger picture of how language evolved.

THE RED HERRING OF THE LARYNX

Let's begin by looking at the species that is genetically closest to us: the chimpanzee. Decades of experiments have repeatedly shown that chimpanzees raised in close contact with humans will never speak.

It's not because the apes are not intelligent—they demonstrate the capacity for manipulating tools and solving puzzles—but speech eludes them because they lack a very specific ability to reproduce sounds they hear in their environment: vocal learning.

One school of thought asserts that in humans, the descended larynx, which sits lower within the throat than in other species, allows for more diverse vocal tract shapes. This, in turn, enables the vocalisation of vowels and consonants that are the key elements of speech. It was thus argued that the difference between us and other organisms lay in the anatomy and resultant acoustics of the vocal tract.

But this was a conclusion drawn from very old studies of anatomy based on dead animals, and I have always been hesitant to judge what a living animal can do by analysing its dissected corpse. So, when I was a post-doctoral research fellow at Harvard University, I joined forces with evolutionary biologist Alfred Crompton to visualise, using X-rays, how the vocal tract moves and changes when living animals make their sounds.

In all the mammals we studied, ranging from goats to dogs, the larynx descends during vocalisation to produce an anatomical configuration resembling the human vocal tract. More recently, working with Asif Ghazanfar and Bart de Boer, we repeated the experiments with living monkeys and used those X-ray videos to produce a computer model of a monkey's vocal tract. We were able to simulate the monkey's vocal range to show that non-human primates should be able to produce many intelligible vowels—and yet they don't. This suggests that the seat of human language is not in vocal anatomy, and that we are barking up the wrong tree if we think that vocal anatomy explains the eloquence of our species.

PAGE 160
Head and neck magnetic resonance imaging scan showing the vocal tract, which is used to produce sound.

BELOW
Chimpanzees possess the vocal anatomy needed for producing intelligible vowels, yet are unable to speak as humans do.

MAKING THE RIGHT CONNECTIONS

So what keeps monkeys or chimpanzees from imitating speech? We can take a hint from Charles Darwin, who suggested that our linguistic prowess may stem from the neural wiring connecting the brain and vocal tract.

In most mammals, including non-human primates, the connections between the motor cortex in the brain and the motor neurons that control structures in the vocal tract, such as the larynx and the tongue, are indirect. Motor neurons from the motor cortex project to interneurons in the brain stem, and it is those interneurons that then link up to the motor neurons controlling the vocal tract.

But humans, in addition to having these indirect connections, also possess direct cortical-to-motor-neuron connections. Are these direct connections responsible for the ability to produce speech? This question can be answered with empirical evidence, using the broad comparative approach I mentioned earlier.

Many different species have independently evolved the capacity to imitate and produce sounds, and sometimes even speech. Parrots immediately come to mind, but vocal imitation has also been recorded in mammals. A famous harbour seal by the name of Hoover was known to holler "Hello there!" and "Get over here!" with a gruff Maine accent it picked up from New England native George Swallow, who raised the seal as a pup.

If the hypothesis that direct cortical-to-motor-neuron connections enable vocal imitation is correct, then such connections should be present in animals that can imitate speech, and absent in those that cannot. Indeed, this prediction has been upheld in songbirds and parrots, which have direct connections between the avian equivalent of the motor cortex and the neurons that control the syrinx (analogous to the larynx in mammals). Other birds that aren't vocal learners or cannot imitate speech, such as chickens, don't have these connections.

IT'S ALL IN YOUR HEAD

But speech does not represent the totality of language; it is just one of the output modalities of language, not language itself. Parroting speech is different from understanding the rules, principles and processes that govern how words are strung together to form sentences—what we call grammar or syntax.

All animals studied to date only recognise and use what is known as finite-state grammar, where sentences are generated word by word in a linear manner—for example, 'The cat ate the mouse'. Humans, on the other hand, employ more complex, supra-regular grammars, which have a hierarchical rule structure to allow for the insertion of clauses: 'The cat that chased the dog ate the mouse'. This significantly raises the upper bound of expressivity in human language.

What is the neural basis for these abilities? Considerable evidence points to a part of the prefrontal cortex called Broca's area, which is larger and more connected in humans than in other primates.

Neurobiologist Natalie Schenker has found that Broca's area is the most expanded cortical region known in the human brain relative to our primate cousins. Meanwhile, using functional magnetic resonance imaging, cognitive scientist Christophe Pallier and many others have found that Broca's area becomes increasingly active when parsing grammatically complex sentences. Finally, neuroscientist James Rilling has shown that Broca's area is much more strongly and widely connected to other parts of the brain, like the parietal and temporal cortex, in humans than in other primates. Collectively, these data clearly point towards a role for Broca's expansion in the neural basis for human syntax.

> Parroting speech is different from understanding the rules, principles and processes that govern how words are strung together to form sentences— what we call grammar or syntax.

SPEAKING IN CODE

The broad comparative approach, coupled with brain imaging data, has yielded insights into the neural structures that enable language acquisition in humans. However, to ultimately understand the evolution of language, we must delve into the lingua franca of all life on earth—DNA.

In many ways, the genetic code is analogous to language. A finite number of DNA bases can be strung together in myriad ways to give rise to all forms of living organisms. There are rules governing how this string is composed and interpreted: base pairing only occurs between A and T and between G and C, and genes are read as a triplet code with an internal punctuation system of start and stop codons—a grammar of sorts. Moreover, genes, like words with useful meanings, get passed down, sometimes with modifications, from one generation to the next, thus adding to the richness of the lexicon of life.

Presumably, there are word variants within this genetic lexicon that confer upon humans our unique faculty of language. One key candidate gene that has emerged from comparative genetic studies is *FOXP2*. The human variant of *FOXP2*, shared by all human populations, is different from chimpanzees and other primates, and its disruption results in severe speech impediments. It was the first gene to be discovered that has a clear relationship with spoken language ability.

> To ultimately understand the evolution of language, we must delve into the lingua franca of all life on earth—DNA.

More importantly, the discovery of the human *FOXP2* variant allows scientists to explore *when* human language evolved. From recently sequenced Denisovan and Neanderthal genomes, we learnt that the human *FOXP2* variant was already present half a million years ago in our common ancestor with these hominins. This not only raises the possibility that our ancient relatives may have been equipped for speech; it also means that it is possible for us to begin piecing together the origins of human language from DNA sequences.

Without a doubt, there is much more to understand about the genes that underlie complex, human-specific linguistic behaviours such as syntax or semantics. But the good news is that scientists are now better equipped than ever to test hypotheses about the evolution of language. As more fossil DNA sequences come to light, I am optimistic that they will yield real insights into the genetic, neurological and cultural evolutionary transitions that have made us the most articulate animal on Earth.

Tecumseh Fitch *is professor of cognitive biology at the University of Vienna, Austria. An evolutionary biologist and cognitive scientist, his research revolves around bioacoustics and biolinguistics, with a specific focus on vertebrate vocal production in relation to the evolution of speech and music in our own species.*

This chapter is based on 'The Evolution of the Biological Capacity to Acquire Language', a talk given by Tecumseh Fitch on 14 August 2017 in Singapore as part of the *10-on-10: The Chronicles of Evolution* lecture series. The material here was abstracted and edited by Jeremy Chan.

FURTHER READING

Enard et al. (2002) Molecular evolution of *FOXP2*, a gene involved in speech and language. *Nature.* 10.1038/nature01025

Hauser et al. (2002) The faculty of language: what is it, who has it, and how did it evolve? *Science.* 10.1126/science.298.5598.1569

Fitch (2010) *The evolution of language*. Cambridge: Cambridge University Press.

Schenker et al. (2010) Broca's area homologue in chimpanzees (*Pan troglodytes*): probabilistic mapping, asymmetry, and comparison to humans. *Cerebral Cortex.* 10.1093/cercor/bhp138

Pallier et al. (2011) Cortical representation of the constituent structure of sentences. *Proceedings of the National Academy of Sciences of the United States of America.* 10.1073/pnas.1018711108

Stobbe et al. (2012) Visual artificial grammar learning: comparative research on humans, kea (*Nestor notabilis*) and pigeons (*Columba livia*). *Philosophical Transactions of the Royal Society B: Biological Sciences.* 10.1098/rstb.2012.0096

Chapter 15

Years before
present

10^{10}

10^{9}

10^{8}

THE LOGIC OF
CULTURAL
EVOLUTION

10^{7}

10^{6}

10^{5}

Why the material matters

The logic of evolutionary theory can help us understand how
human culture arrived at where we are today, and where we are
headed next.

10^{4}

10^{3}

Roland Fletcher

10^{2}

10^{1}

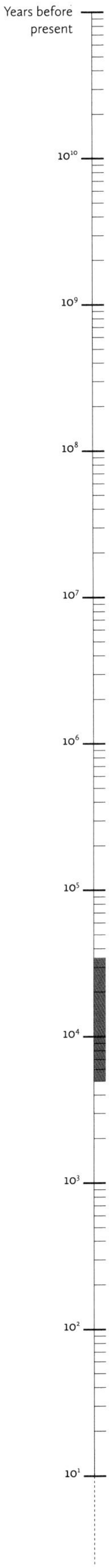

PAGE 170

Stone Age blade
fragments. Stone
tools leave a
permanent mark
on the landscape.

As the preceding chapters demonstrate, Darwin's theory of evolution has been extraordinarily successful at explaining the biology of human beings. Distant events in our past—from the Big Bang to how fish left the water and how primates evolved large brains—all start to make sense when seen in the light of evolution.

But being human is much more than having a set of human genes. What it means to be human also includes how individual humans interact with one another, involving social behaviour expressed through language, art and civilisation, which we collectively call culture. Unlike our biological characteristics, culture is not transmitted genetically, but is passed down from generation to generation through social interactions and in a milieu of material objects and structures.

There is serious debate in fields such as anthropology about whether culture itself is subject to evolutionary processes. I would argue that the evolutionary approach is indeed an appropriate conceptual tool to use when studying culture, but only if we recognise the significance and role of the material. The material refers to artefacts and structures which have often been overlooked because they are regarded as by-products of the mind, when they are in fact crucial variables in their own right that have an impact on our behaviour.

LEAVING A MARK

For example, the use of tools has historically been understood to be an indicator of a particular stage of cultural evolution, a consequence of social behaviour rather than something that could trigger a change. However, if we consider the evolution of the material itself, we see that tools are both functional objects and signals used to demarcate territory, and that tools in fact changed how hominins interacted with each other.

Among the great apes, gorillas define space on the ground by flattening rings of vegetation around their sleeping places, creating camp sites. This form of spatial organisation is a basal higher-primate behaviour that would have preceded the acquisition of tool use in hominins. Even today, the ordered spacing of towels on a beach shows how embedded this patterning is in our behaviour. Chimpanzees, meanwhile, show that the great apes also use stone tools, as did early hominins. Our ancestors combined both types of behaviour three to four million years ago. However, we are different from chimpanzees because hominins made stone tools wherever they went, creating the highly visible patches of their camps that we can still see today.

> There is serious debate in fields such as anthropology about whether culture itself is subject to evolutionary processes.

The important thing about stone tools is that they are durable, leaving a permanent mark on the landscape. In contrast, other means of marking territory are primarily organic and disappear very rapidly, as with the gorillas. This means that if a hominin went into an unfamiliar area, it could know that other hominins had been there. By observing differences in the shapes of the tools, they could also tell whether or not those tools had been made by themselves or some other unrelated hominins, even if they never met them.

That the ability to signal presence through stone tools was a significant one is supported by the existence of gigantoliths, strangely large tools that were impractical to use but impossible to miss. What these large stone tools suggest is that there was a very powerful selective pressure on the visibility of tools, causing them to become more differentiated in form, and some to become more distinctly visible.

In other words, once introduced into hominin behaviour, tools became a new variable in their own right. They introduced new, enduring signals about who was where, selecting in favour of larger brains that could process and recall more spatial data and make decisions based on it. Predicting whether to seek or avoid hominins you know about but who have not seen you was a powerful agent in subsequent cultural evolution. The tools created spatial landscapes that selected in favour of larger brains, which could then manage the burgeoning spatial signals.

......

HELLO FROM THE OTHER SIDE

The next major development in human culture was the use of fire. One very good reason to be unafraid of fire is that if you follow behind a bushfire, you will get a lot of high-yield cooked food for very little effort. However, the ability to control fire confers more than just cooked food; the real significance of fire, once you can make it, is that it tells other hominins where you are and you where they are. What fire introduces is the capacity to observe a cultural landscape over huge distances, allowing hominins to interact without needing to meet one another. This advantage would powerfully and preferentially select for hominins with the brain capacity to deal with the geometry of understanding the large landscape that smoke signals and the light from campfires provide.

> The effect of the material transformation of creating art was to end the selective advantage of bigger brains.

A similar benefit is conferred by hominins' use of colour to mark their bodies, which also gave them the ability to deliver a social message at a distance. Once hominins started creating marks and shapes from about 70,000 years ago, the size and elaboration of their camps increased substantially. Apart from marking themselves, hominins also marked objects around them, leaving complex geometric patterns on bones and paintings on cave walls. Some of these marks recorded periodicities, allowing information about times between seasons, reproductive sequences and so on to be stored outside the human brain.

The effect of the material transformation of creating art was to end the selective advantage of bigger brains. This was crucial because modern humans were already in a situation where the size of the head at birth was (and is) very close to the size of the birth canal through the female pelvis. In chimpanzees, by contrast, the ratio is smaller, and giving birth is much less problematic or risky. Material thus provided the human body with a way out of a 'size trap'

of increasing brain size, which its impact on human behaviour had preferentially selected for.

......

BIGGER BRAINS, BIGGER GROUPS

As hominin cognitive abilities increased, so did the size of their social groups. Over the past 10,000 years, hominins have gone from behaving like small-group animals such as the oryx to behaving like wildebeest, which form gigantic herds. We have tended to assume that this growth in group size had to do with the sociality of hominins, but when we look at it in material terms, we realise that it is actually enabled by the materials that hominins use.

Hominin group sizes have undergone three major transitions: first, from hunter-gatherer communities to sedentary agrarian communities; second, the development of agrarian-based urbanism; and finally, the rise of industrialised cities. Each of these transitions was preceded by material changes that were requirements for the next step in cultural evolution.

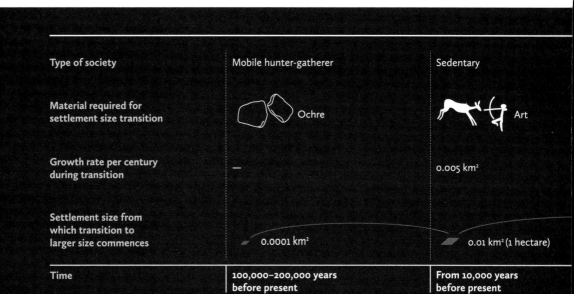

Type of society	Mobile hunter-gatherer	Sedentary
Material required for settlement size transition	Ochre	Art
Growth rate per century during transition	—	0.005 km²
Settlement size from which transition to larger size commences	0.0001 km²	0.01 km² (1 hectare)
Time	100,000–200,000 years before present	From 10,000 years before present

For example, the material characteristics that made sedentary life possible—periodicity marking, durable walls to block out sound, and colour-coding—were already present in late-Pleistocene hominins 20,000 years ago. However, it was only about 10,000 years ago, during the mobile-to-sedentary transition, that these characteristics came together and started transforming the workings of our societies and the magnitudes of our communities. This led to settlements larger than one hectare in extent, which used agriculture.

The subsequent development of agrarian-based urbanism from 5,000 years ago resulted in compact settlements with sizes beyond one square kilometre, allowing communities of up to a million people. This likewise depended on materials developed well before the transition—things like large monuments, calendars and sign systems. The third transition to industrial urbanism, which resulted in settlements larger than 100 square kilometres, only occurred about 200 years ago, and first required a whole suite of new material— information managers like clocks and mechanised printing—before cities of tens of millions of people could develop.

Changes in material facilities were a precondition for the formation of larger and larger settlements and communities, not

BELOW
Hominin group sizes have already gone through three major transitions, and are moving towards a fourth. Historically, as maximum settlement size goes up 100 times, the rate of growth of settlements goes up 1,000 times.

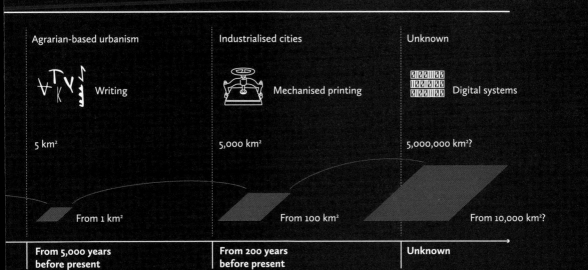

Agrarian-based urbanism	Industrialised cities	Unknown
Writing	Mechanised printing	Digital systems
5 km²	5,000 km²	5,000,000 km²?
From 1 km²	From 100 km²	From 10,000 km²?
From 5,000 years before present	**From 200 years before present**	**Unknown**

derivatives of their growth or merely an indicator of the existence of complex social life.

......

AGENTS OF ACCELERATION

While the first mobile-to-sedentary transition was very slow, the next successive size jumps happened much faster; we are currently in a period of a steep take-off, moving towards a fourth transition. If you consider the time taken for these changes to occur, you will notice that the rate of growth of settlements goes up by 1,000 times when the maximum size goes up 100 times. This is where our analysis starts to become troubling.

Following the logic of an accelerating rate of growth, the next transition, to compact settlements larger than 10,000 square kilometres in extent, whenever it happens, will occur at an expansion rate of five million square kilometres per century, meaning that there could be single cities well over half the size of the entire country of Australia a century after the transition. If the pressures of our recent transition to the industrial age are anything to go by, this next transition will be difficult to say the least.

No one anticipated how clocks and pocket watches—originally developed between the 14th and the 16th centuries to manage religious activity and meet the demands of status-obsessed European elites, respectively—would become key parts of the industrial transition in the 19th century. In the same way, we live in an intriguing time where some material device we are now using for something quite mundane—perhaps for colouring chewing gum!—could just turn out to be the power source of the future.

Because material things are the unanticipated preconditions for large future societal shifts, a series of unrecognised transformations lie hidden inside the everyday material around us—and these will be the true drivers of the future.

Roland Fletcher *is professor of theoretical and world archaeology at the University of Sydney, Australia, where he is the instigator and director of the Angkor Research Programme. He is the author of* The Limits of Settlement Growth: A Theoretical Outline, *which put forth a radical new way of understanding cultural evolution. In 2007, he was a distinguished fellow of Durham University's Institute of Advanced Study.*

This chapter is based on 'Hominin Cultural Evolution: Pattern and Process over Four Million Years', a talk given by Roland Fletcher on 18 September 2017 in Singapore as part of the *10-on-10: The Chronicles of Evolution* lecture series. The material here was abstracted and edited by Rebecca Tan.

FURTHER READING

Fletcher (2003) Barbed wire was an invention to control American cows: what is required in a neo-Darwinian theory of cultural behaviour? *Cambridge Archaeological Journal*. 10.1017/S0959774303240166

Fletcher (2006) Materiality, space, time, and outcome. In: *A companion to archaeology* (ed. Bintliff). Oxford: Blackwell Publishing.

Fletcher (2007) *The limits of settlement growth: a theoretical outline*. Cambridge: Cambridge University Press.

Fletcher (2010) Urban materialities: meaning, magnitude, friction, and outcomes. In: *The Oxford handbook of material culture studies* (eds. Hicks and Beaudry). New York: Oxford University Press.

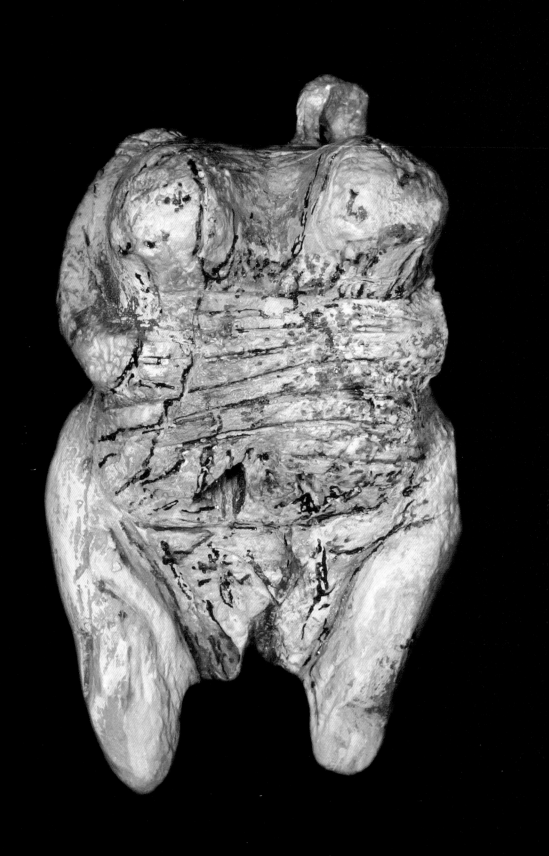

Chapter 16

GOING WITH THE (INFORMATION) FLOW

How information processing governs the past, present and future of our species

From physical tools to tools for thought, our ability and need
to process information has driven the development of human
societies throughout the ages.

Sander van der Leeuw

10^{10}

10^{9}

10^{8}

10^{7}

10^{6}

10^{5}

10^{4}

10^{3}

10^{2}

10^{1}

When seeking answers to questions about human evolution, the biological perspective has yielded invaluable insights. But as an archaeologist, I am of the view that, while crucial to piecing together the past, genetics and anatomy are not the only things that matter in the very long history of our species.

An important outgrowth of human biology is human society, which is incredibly complex and interconnected. From my perspective, human society is a relationship between three different flows: those of energy, matter and information. Of the three, energy and matter cannot be shared on a social scale—only information can be freely transmitted, and that is what creates our cultures and ways of doing things.

Notably, these three flows interact in an interesting way. We need energy and matter (in the form of resources) to live. Information allows us to create new and better ways to harness energy and matter. I argue, then, that it is information processing that helps build societies and keeps them functioning. It is what has allowed us to organise ourselves, our ideas and our environments to achieve the state of human society that we have today.

> From my perspective, human society is a relationship between three different flows: those of energy, matter and information.

NOT CAST IN STONE

Far from being a static entity, information processing has changed dramatically over the millennia. These changes occurred in stages, the first of which was the development of biological cognitive capacity—the evolution of the human brain. Earlier chapters have dealt with this topic in detail, but here I would like to introduce the concept of short-term working memory (STWM), which refers to the number of information sources that can be processed simultaneously.

We have deduced that chimpanzees have an STWM in the range of 1 to 3. They know how to use a hammerstone and an anvil to crack a nut. Humans, on the other hand, have an average STWM of 7. This can be inferred from the changing nature of stone tools from the Palaeolithic age (approximately 2.6 million years ago) to the present.

Early humans first began to make tools by using a hammerstone to take a flake off the edge of another stone, discarding the flake and using the stone, which now has a pointy tip. The point is a zero-dimensional way of looking at objects, like drawing a dot on a piece of paper. In this case, the toolmaker needs an STWM of 3—he or she must simultaneously process information about the hammerstone, the angle of each stroke of the hammerstone, and the desired product.

Then, by taking multiple adjacent flakes off the stone, our ancestors learnt to create a one-dimensional line. In doing so, they were incorporating a fourth information source: the sequence of blows with the hammerstone in a specific direction. They eventually proceeded to chip off material all around the stone, creating a surface in two dimensions. The ability to distinguish between the line and the surface raised the STWM to 5.

PAGE 180
Carved out of mammoth ivory an estimated 40,000 years ago, the six-centimetre-tall Venus of Hohle Fels is thought to be the oldest known sculpture of a human figure.

Zero dimensions: point

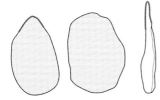

First dimension: line

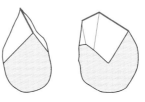

LEFT
As early humans became adept at processing more sources of information, the tools they made also incorporated more dimensions.

Second dimension: surface

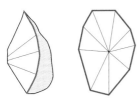

Third dimension: volume

Finally, around 300,000 years ago, humans started treating pieces of stone in three dimensions, taking into consideration not just line and surface, but also volume. They also became capable of serial tool production, which meant that the toolmaker had to bear in mind a future tool during the manufacturing process. Around 50,000 years ago, humans attained an average STWM of 7, and this has been sufficient for all the cognitive needs of modern humans.

Therefore, using stone tools as a proxy for the development of biological cognitive capacity, we can tell that it took two million years for humans to attain this apparently basic level of information processing.

INTELLIGENCE IN NUMBERS

The next quantum leap in information processing came with the shift to collective learning at the start of the Upper Palaeolithic period. Based on the fossil record, we can conclude that larger groups of early humans were interacting during that time. There was a strong emphasis on communication, and I would argue that it was then that language became essential to further human development.

Materially, this period in history saw a huge explosion of new inventions, which coincided with migrations—humans began to colonise parts of the world with harsh climates previously considered uninhabitable. The dispersal of human populations meant that different groups in different places interacted much more with themselves than with others. Cultural differences thus emerged, bringing colour and diversity to the palette of humanity. Each group developed its own unique ways of adapting to the environment, obtaining food and building shelter.

Underscoring all these events was the acquisition of a whole set of tools for thought. The ability to distinguish reality from conception is one such tool for thought, and it allowed humans to mentally generate potential events and consider multiple alternative responses to those events. They also learnt to sort objects based on similarities and differences. Furthermore, in cave paintings, such as those of the Lascaux Cave in southwestern France, we see evidence that our ancestors became capable of translating a three-dimensional observation into a two-dimensional image.

With these tools for thought, a positive feedback loop emerges in information processing. When encountering a new situation, humans begin to categorise and solve problems, which increases the number of tools for thought available to acquire and structure knowledge. With more knowledge, humans begin to notice more problems, which call for the application of existing tools for thought, or the creation of new ones. New knowledge is once again obtained, and the cycle repeats itself.

Eventually, the limits of individual information processing are reached. People then start interacting with others, leveraging the information processing capacity of the group to solve problems. This requires more matter and energy to be gathered from the environment. How is this achieved? With even more information processing. Hence, once we move from the individual to the collective, growing populations and growing resource requirements are inevitable.

BELOW
Cave paintings from the Lascaux Cave, France.

A TIME TO SETTLE DOWN

As populations grew, groups of people began to abandon the hunter-gatherer lifestyle and settle down around 10,000 years ago. This period in history is referred to as the Neolithic revolution.

There are many arguments suggesting that this change in lifestyle was due to the coming of the Holocene, when the climate became more stable and the environment more suitable for settlement. I argue, however, that the shift from a roaming lifestyle to a sedentary one is fundamentally a conceptual change in the way humans interacted with the environment.

Until that point in time, humans had taken from the environment whatever presented itself as ripe and ready to eat or use. From the Neolithic revolution onwards, however, humans were no longer only reacting to the environment, but proactively changing it, clearing fields, planting crops and creating dedicated spaces for particular activities.

During this process, populations continued to grow, and there was more communication and collaboration. But this growth came at a huge cost—social conflicts emerged, necessitating the invention of institutions and sets of social rules for people to obey if they wanted to remain part of society. The need to solve the problem of social conflict thus ended up demanding even more information processing, and this further drove the aggregation of populations, eventually resulting in the formation of towns and cities.

OPPOSITE
The 11,000-year-old ruins of Göbekli Tepe, Turkey, considered by some researchers to be the site of the oldest temple in the world.

A CASCADE OF CONSEQUENCES

We often talk about how problems create solutions, but the inverse is also true—solutions can create problems. Laws and systems of administration help societies cope with conflict, but such organisation is costly in energy, which needs to be obtained from the environment. So what I imagine—and this is a relatively abstract concept—is that you get an outward flow of information processing to the periphery

> Reality has many more dimensions than those we are aware of even collectively, so when we create solutions to problems, unintended consequences occur.

of society, and an inward flow of energy and matter to its centre.

These dynamics drive human societies to further intervene and encroach on the environment, triggering consequences at temporal scales that we cannot observe. To use a modern example, Henry Ford, when he created the first car, never imagined what it would be like to have three billion of them on Earth. We trade short-term risks for long-term ones, and I argue that our propensity to do this stems from the limitation of our STWM to 7.

Our minds can individually process seven to eight dimensions. Collectively, as a group, this number increases. But reality has many more dimensions than those we are aware of even collectively, so when we create solutions to problems, unintended consequences occur.

Eventually, we arrive at tipping points—for instance, sustainability is now an issue because our behaviour in the past has driven us to a point where we can no longer control the wide-ranging impacts of our actions on the environment. If we are to deal with these tipping points effectively, we must fundamentally change our thinking. We must move away from a reductionist approach to problems, towards an approach that can account for the complexity of systems.

Technology is a key enabler for understanding complex and adaptive systems, with advanced computers allowing us to transcend the limits of our STWM and mine data, so that we can better inform our actions and extrapolate their consequences on the environment. Harnessed appropriately, technology could increase our information processing capacity without a corresponding or proportionate increase in energy and matter. Whether humans can innovate ourselves out of our present predicament remains an open question, but in trying to answer that question, we may bring about the next significant step in the evolution of our species and society.

An expert in complex, adaptive systems, **Sander van der Leeuw** *has conducted archaeological and environmental fieldwork in the Near East, Syria, Holland, France, Mexico, and recently China and Japan. He is the founding director of the School of Human Evolution and Social Change at Arizona State University in the US, and is currently co-director of its Complex Adaptive Systems Initiative. Van der Leeuw's research revolves around the role of invention, innovation and sustainability in societies across the globe.*

This chapter is based on 'The Evolution of Innovation', a talk given by Sander van der Leeuw on 13 October 2017 in Singapore as part of the *10-on-10: The Chronicles of Evolution* lecture series. The material here was abstracted and edited by Jeremy Chan.

FURTHER READING

van der Leeuw (2007) Information processing and its role in the rise of the European world system. In: *Sustainability or collapse?* (eds. Costanza, Graumlich and Steffen). Cambridge: MIT Press.

Read et al. (2015) The extension of social relations in time and space during the Palaeolithic. In: *Settlement, society and cognition in human evolution* (eds. Coward, Hosfield, Pope and Wenban-Smith). Cambridge: Cambridge University Press.

Chapter 17

LINGO WITH A LIFE OF ITS OWN

The dynamic, living entity that is language

Biological evolution gave rise to the human faculty for language, but language itself also evolves as it is transmitted among individuals and across generations.

N. J. Enfield

Years before present
10^{10}
10^{9}
10^{8}
10^{7}
10^{6}
10^{5}
10^{4}
10^{3}
10^{2}
10^{1}

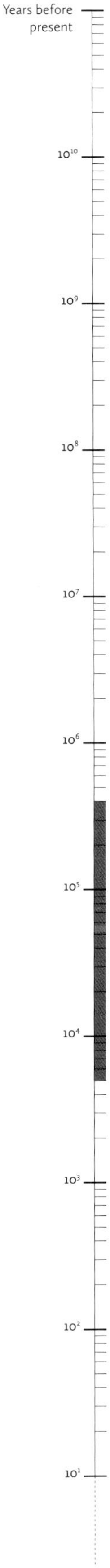

PAGE 190
Cuneiform
inscriptions from
Persepolis, Iran.
Cuneiform, which
emerged an
estimated 5,000
years ago, is one of
the earliest systems
of writing.

Speaking a language comes instinctively to most individuals. In contrast, speaking *about* language is much less intuitive. Multiple phenomena are involved in the production and use of language, making it challenging to articulate why language is the way it is and how it came to be.

Depending on how one approaches the topic, explanations for the evolution of language can take on very different forms. For example, a biological account would contain evidence of physical and cognitive adaptations emerging on the timescale of millennia. In contrast, a social-cultural narrative would highlight linguistic innovations and how they propagate within or between communities over years, decades or centuries.

Regardless of which perspective one takes, it is clear that language is a product of history. To understand its evolution is to delve into the historical events that have led to its current form. The concepts of inheritance and transmission are thus important to both biology and language.

A QUESTION OF INHERITANCE

When Charles Darwin contemplated the evolution of language, he likened languages to species in the natural world, suggesting that the rules for speciation and those for language diversification were analogous. Speciation in biology is often depicted as a tree diagram summarising the evolutionary relationships among species. At a glance, one can infer common ancestry and descent with modification. Similar tree diagrams have been constructed to track the evolutionary lineage of parent languages and their derivative forms.

Such diagrams treat languages as whole units, where the entire language system is inherited during branching events. But are languages necessarily transmitted as whole units? This can only be true if the evolution of language is viewed as strictly analogous to the evolution of vertebrates—organisms such as birds, fish and mammals.

In the context of vertebrate evolution, the genome is passed down from parent to offspring as a complete set. But such vertical transmission of whole, intact genomes does not apply to all living organisms. Many forms of life exchange component parts of their genomes—even individual genes—horizontally; bacteria are a case in point.

In the same vein, language need not be inherited as a monolithic whole. Take, for example, the word 'kangaroo'. It can be cited or borrowed by any language, even when the borrower does not adopt the entire language system from which 'kangaroo' originated. Hence, I argue that the horizontal transmission of linguistic items, such as individual words or grammatical forms, must also be considered in discussions about the evolution of language.

Nonetheless, it should be noted that the word 'kangaroo' cannot exist in a vacuum. It is given meaning by other words associated with it, such as the words 'jump', 'pouch' or 'Australia'. In the same way a screwdriver doesn't make sense in the absence of a screw, functional relations exist between linguistic items, like the word 'kangaroo', and the systems they belong to. These functional relations have implications on how successfully a linguistic item will propagate and persist within a language system.

> In the same way a screwdriver doesn't make sense in the absence of a screw, functional relations exist between linguistic items.

OF BRIDGES AND BIASES

Whether or not a linguistic item becomes a stable feature of a language system depends on transmission biases that either favour or hinder its population-wide uptake. Before we explore what these transmission biases are, we must first acknowledge that a word does not exist solely in the mind of the one who invented or chanced upon it. Rather, it repeatedly shuttles between the private space of the mind and the public space of conversation, sometimes even leaving a material trace on the physical world.

I know a word in my mind (private) and I use it in conversation with another individual (public). The listener internalises the word and its attached meaning (private). He or she then goes on to use the word in other conversations (public), and the process repeats itself. This is known as a social cognitive causal chain.

Based on this chain, we can infer that any disruption in the process will stop the word from becoming embedded in a language system. I argue that there are four 'bridges' that each novel word has to cross to continue along the chain.

> A word repeatedly shuttles between the private space of the mind and the public space of conversation, sometimes even leaving a material trace on the physical world.

The first bridge is exposure, and at this juncture we can observe multiple transmission biases in action. In the bias of social connectedness, people who are more socially connected are more likely to encounter new words, and are also more likely to expose others to what they encounter. Other biases at this stage include those relating to salience and social identity; people pay closer attention to stimuli that are relevant to them, or to individuals they deem important.

After getting past the first bridge, the word must then be represented or stored in a person's mind. How easily a new word is committed to memory has to do with its integration with pre-existing knowledge—a context bias. At the same time, the utility of the new word also affects its likelihood of internalisation—a content bias.

Content bias also plays a role in the next bridge, which involves the reproduction of a word. If a new word helps me achieve a particular goal in my social interactions, I will use it over other words I already know. Words that signal conformity may also have a greater chance of being reproduced in social contexts.

Finally, the material manifestation of the word significantly affects the dynamics of its transmission. When spoken, a word fades quickly from consciousness. Written down, however, its persistence

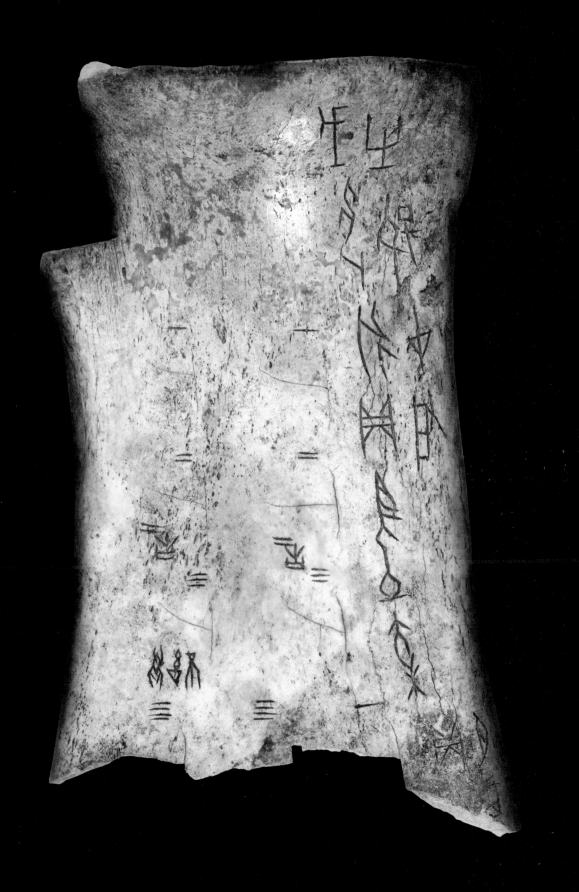

TABULA COMBINATORIA

In qua ex probatissimis Authoribus primævorum Characterum formæ eorum-que Omnium, qui ab ijs Originem duxerunt successiva temporum propa-gatione exhibentur; Ex quibus luculenter deducitur Omnia linguarum Alpha-beta, nonnulla in se priscarum literarum vestigia tenere.

Valor Litera-rum.	Character du-plex mysticus ab Angelis tra-ditus dicitur.	Character tem-pore transi-tus fluminis Authore R. Abrahamo Babnis.	Characterum vete-rum Samaritanorum formæ variè ex nummis extractæ aliisque Authoribus.	Floridus Character Sa-maritanorum ex Vil-alpando nummisque ex-tractus.	Character Mosaicô quo legem in tabu-lis scripsit ex va-riis Rabbinorû mo-mentis deprompt.	Charac-ter Sy-riacus.	Character verus He-bræus si-ve Assy-rius
A							
B							
C							
D							
H							
V							
Z							
Ch							
T							
I							
C							
L							
M							
N							
S							
Ayn							
P							
Ts							
QK							
R							
Sch							
Th							

is substantially increased. Collectively, these bridges and biases determine whether linguistic innovations eventually assimilate into language systems and cause them to evolve.

STABILITY AMID CHAOS

Over time, speech habits and linguistic behaviours stabilise within a community and become relatively impermeable to external influence. Having explained how change is gradually effected in language systems, we now visit the question of how such stability arises. What are some of the forces that cause language systems to hold together as coherent structures?

The first of these forces is known as sociometric closure, which arises from the trade-off between the number of social interactions and the strength of each interaction. Individuals must invest time—a limited resource—into maintaining relationships. This imposes an upper bound on the number of relationships each person can effectively maintain, resulting in corresponding constraints on the diffusion of linguistic items through a community. Members of a community thus end up circulating a common set of linguistic items, creating a closed economy of speech habits and linguistic behaviours.

But even as linguistic items circulate in social networks, they compete with one another to be used during communication. The German scholar and linguist Max Müller wrote in 1870 that "a struggle for life is constantly going on amongst the words and grammatical forms in each language". This struggle is especially apparent with words that can be used to express the same intent. We rank these words according to their inherent characteristics, such as word length and how effective a word is at performing a specific function, which in turn affect their frequency of use. In creating these criteria, we are essentially building relations among words, and by defining words relative to one another in a set, we inadvertently cause them to behave more like a system than individual items.

OPPOSITE
17th-century
linguistics table.

In addition to relations among words, there exists an interdependence between the structure of a linguistic item and the context within which it fits. Each time we produce an utterance (for example, in the form of a sentence), we not only communicate all the meanings of its component parts, but also advertise the combinatorial relations that those items have. A layer of rules—grammatical structures—is broadcast in tandem with words, and novel linguistic items must obey these rules if they are to be incorporated into a language system.

> Anthropologists have hypothesised that language was born of a need to manage social networks in a more efficient manner.

BUILT TO LAST

The dynamics observed in the evolution of language would not be possible without the social aspect of transmission. Anthropologists have hypothesised that language was born of a need to manage social networks in a more efficient manner. The use and transmission of early language presumably involved personal verbal exchanges among individuals, which, as mentioned earlier, is time-consuming and limits the maximum size of social networks.

These constraints were eased with the invention of writing and print. By capturing words and their functional relations in the material domain, non-personal exposure to linguistic items and innovations became possible. Language systems could persist and permeate populations more effectively with the advent of the written word, enabling the growth of social networks.

In modern times, social networks span the globe, and linguistic innovations have the opportunity to diffuse via more channels than ever before. High population densities and pervasive media also provide the conditions for passive visual and auditory exposure to novel linguistic items. Hence, language continues to evolve in the present day, and this is surely not the end of the story.

N. J. Enfield *is a professor of linguistics at the University of Sydney,*
Australia, and the director of the Sydney Social Sciences and Humanities
Advanced Research Centre. An expert in Southeast Asian languages,
his research interests revolve around the dynamic relationships among
language, culture, cognition and social interaction.

This chapter is based on 'The Evolutions of Language', a talk given by N.J. Enfield on 14 August 2017
in Singapore as part of the *10-on-10: The Chronicles of Evolution* lecture series. The material here
was abstracted and edited by Jeremy Chan.

FURTHER READING

Hill and Dunbar (2003) Social network size in humans. *Human Nature.* 10.1007/s12110-003-1016-y

Enfield (2008) Transmission biases in linguistic epidemiology. *Journal of Language Contact.*
10.1163/000000008792525273

Enfield (2014) *Natural causes of language: frames, biases and cultural transmission.* Berlin: Language
Science Press.

Chapter 18

Years before
present

10^{10}

10^9

10^8

HOW WE
BECAME
MODERN

10^7

10^6

10^5

The nature and evolution of technology

Technologies evolve in a combinatorial fashion, with each
new technology forming a building block for future inventions.

10^4

10^3

W. Brian Arthur

10^2

10^1

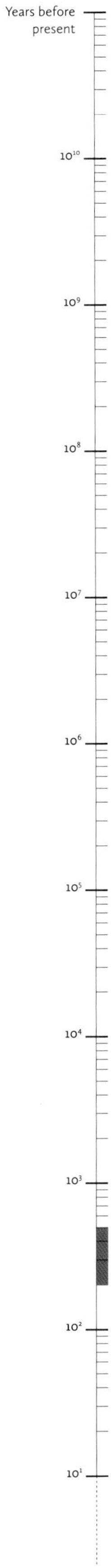

PAGE 200

A water wheel,
an early form of
technology used to
harness the energy
of flowing water.

Consider society and how it functions today—virtually every aspect of it depends on technology. From the physical structures we build to the devices we use, technology has woven itself into the very fabric of human civilisation.

While we often associate technology with tools that are new and cutting-edge, we ought to remember that technology is a collective term, encompassing all the components, methods and processes that have ever existed. By this definition, even ancient people had technology.

Looking back at societies that existed one millennium ago, people already had pulley systems to lift massive loads, brick and mortar with which they built impressive structures, and water wheels that leveraged natural forces to perform work. These technologies may appear primitive, but they contributed significantly to society and the economy during their time.

So technology itself is not new, but the complexity of inventions has increased tremendously. At the same time, the pace of technological advancement has become very rapid. These developments raise interesting questions about the nature of technology and how it co-evolves with society and the economy—questions I have attempted to answer over the course of my career.

......

MAKING THE CASE FOR TECHNOLOGY

> In my mind, technology is *the* killer app that catapulted humanity into modernity.

In his book *Civilisation: The West and the Rest*, Scottish historian Niall Ferguson describes how in the early 15th century, the Ming Dynasty in China and the Ottoman Empire of Turkey were thriving civilisations, while Europe languished in civil unrest and obscurity. Yet, over the course of the next five centuries, Europe leapfrogged the Orient and the Middle East to become the most advanced society in the world. Ferguson attributed Europe's rapid ascendance to six key factors: competition, consumerism, work ethic, property rights, science and medicine.

Conspicuously missing from this mix of ingredients for modernity is technology. But I would argue that, more than anything else, technology is what separates us in the present day from the 1400s. Take away modern housing, modern building construction, cars, modern agriculture, factories and public hygiene, and suddenly you're back in the Middle Ages. In my mind, technology is *the* killer app that catapulted humanity into modernity.

Looking at history, you will find that one of the most significant events to have occurred during the Middle Ages was the print revolution. Prior to the invention of the printing press, all information in Europe was internal to the Church, which meant that the Church had a monopoly on ideas.

Then, a German goldsmith named Johannes Gutenberg came along with his inventions: the hand mould and movable type. This system of interchangeable components, when combined with the screw press, became the first printing press. Gutenberg and others began to print books and make them publicly available, which in turn led to the widespread availability, perusal and discussion of ideas. Independent thinking suddenly became possible. This greatly enhanced the Renaissance, helped bring on the Protestant Reformation, and in due course led to further ideas and inventions. Technology in this case did much to create society and the economy anew.

ABOVE
Gutenberg's printing press enabled ideas to become more widely spread and discussed.

......

COGS IN THE MACHINE OF PROGRESS

Of course, not all technologies bring upheaval to society and the economy—only important ones like the printing press have far-reaching consequences. But important or not, a new technology does not arise by itself from nothing; instead, it derives from a lineage of inventions that came before it. In my research, I have come to understand that all inventions arise from a combination of precursors, and each new technology that appears offers itself up as a component for future inventions.

Returning to Gutenberg's press, the revolutionary device was born of numerous pre-existing tools and methods. To create the block letters of movable type, Gutenberg had to have the means to melt and mould metals. To have a clean surface to print on he used paper; papermaking had arrived in Europe about 100 years before. To apply sufficient pressure onto paper or vellum during the printing process, he had to adapt the screw press, which was common in the winemaking region of Germany where he lived. The printing press therefore arose from a combination of technologies.

Technology evolves in a modular and combinatorial fashion.

The same combinatorial process gave rise to the steam engine. In the late 1600s, Thomas Savery, an English engineer, devised a system consisting of a boiling chamber, pipes and valves which acted in concert to pump water out of coal mines. This design was later modified by another English engineer, Thomas Newcomen, who added a piston to the system, allowing thermal energy to be converted into mechanical motion.

Scottish machinist James Watt then included a separate cold-water condenser to Newcomen's system, greatly increasing the efficiency of steam engines, and suddenly steam engines became commercially viable. Further combinations of technologies resulted in steam-powered mills and steam trains, and by the 1830s a steam-driven Industrial Revolution was in full swing.

From cases like this, we can see that technology is like a set of LEGO blocks which can be assembled into many different structures.

OPPOSITE
Thomas Savery's
steam-driven pump.

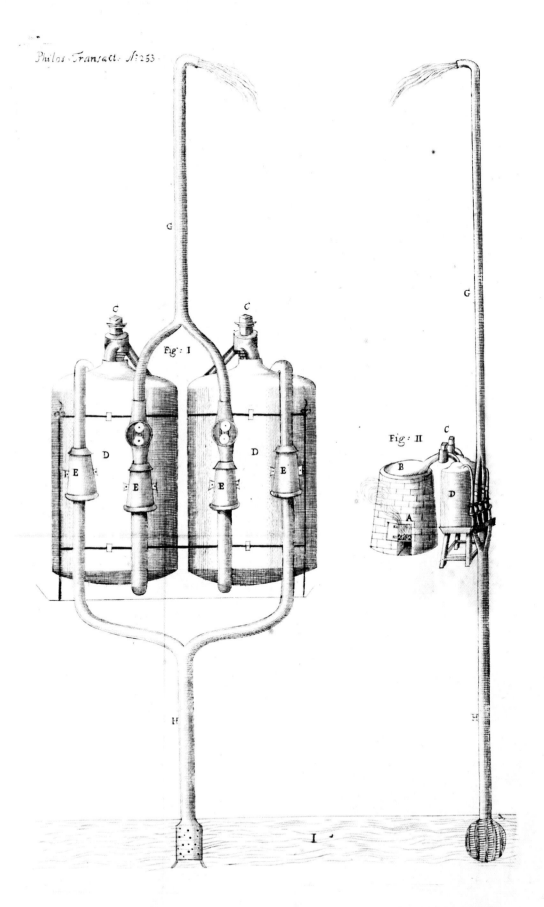

Fig: I

Fig: II

Technology evolves in a modular and combinatorial fashion. The larger the pool of available technologies, the greater the potential for novel inventions; the larger the number of inventions, the greater the pool of available technologies to build from. And as technologies grow in number and sophistication, progress happens.

OPPOSITE
Replica of Newton's 17th century telescope.

A CASCADE OF CONSEQUENCES

The idea of progress is itself relatively recent, becoming widespread only a couple of hundred years ago. Before that, the general perspective was that things simply got better or worse—people understood change, but the notion of change towards constant betterment was alien. It was technology that brought on industrial development and seeded the concept of progress in people's minds.

It also brought on modern science. In 1610, Galileo Galilei discovered sun spots and the phases of Venus using a then-new piece of technology—the telescope. Isaac Newton invented his own form of telescope, and went on to propose a simple mechanism for planetary motions in his 1687 book *Mathematical Principles of Natural Philosophy*. The telescope and the accurate observations of the heavens it yielded opened up the field of astronomy, and brought about a new worldview that the universe was knowable, rational and ordered.

The idea of progress is itself relatively recent, becoming widespread only a couple of hundred years ago.

The new worldview caused a shift around 1760 in attitudes towards the creation of technology. If the entire universe is knowable and ordered, then technology must also be. The fundamental principles of the natural world, gleaned through technology, were used to improve and refine technology itself, as well as spawn new inventions.

We can say from all this that technology forms a vast, self-creating chemistry. It is autopoietic, to borrow a term coined by Chilean biologists Humberto Maturana and Francisco Varela to describe systems capable of producing and maintaining themselves. When combined with the idea that all novel technologies arise from earlier ones—the earliest of which were stones used for crushing, or vines for binding, both available in nature—autopoiesis tells us about how technology emerges and evolves, and also gives us a sense of how the body of technology will continue to expand into the future.

THE PATH BEHIND AND THE ROAD AHEAD

While we may use words typically reserved for living organisms—such as 'self-producing' and 'self-maintaining'—to describe the emergence and evolution of technology, this does not imply that technology is self-deterministic, or that it has consciousness. Technology does not dictate human activity; rather, human inventors and developers create and improve technology to enable us to perform new functions, or to carry out old functions more expediently. Human agency leads, and technology follows.

However, I would like to point out here that the sequence in which technologies appear is important. If, by chance, the order of technological development had been different in the past, the technologies of today would not be as we know them. If Watt's more efficient steam engine had not been invented in the 1760s, steam-powered mills and trains would not have followed as rapidly, and downstream consequences would have been different. The trajectory of future technological and economic advances would inevitably have been altered.

As a corollary to these observations, the value of a piece of technology does not just lie in the function it performs, but also in the possibilities it enables when combined with other available technologies—think of the transistor and the laser in modern times. Only time will tell what new technologies will emerge from this creative ferment, but we can be certain that societies and economies will be transformed in their wake.

W. Brian Arthur *is an external professor at the Santa Fe Institute in the US. A pioneer in complexity economics, Arthur is known for his theoretical work on increasing returns or positive feedbacks in the economy. He was awarded the Schumpeter Prize in Economics in 1990 and the inaugural Lagrange Prize in Complexity Science in 2008. His recent research revolves around the social and economic impact of technology and innovation.*

This chapter is based on 'The Emergence of Technology in Human History', a talk given by W. Brian Arthur on 13 October 2017 in Singapore as part of the *10-on-10: The Chronicles of Evolution* lecture series. The material here was abstracted and edited by Jeremy Chan.

FURTHER READING

Arthur and Polak (2006) The evolution of technology within a simple computer model. *Complexity*. 10.1002/cplx.20130

Arthur (2007) The structure of invention. *Research Policy*. 10.1016/j.respol.2006.11.005

Arthur (2009) *The nature of technology: what it is and how it evolves*. New York: Simon & Schuster.

Chapter 19

10^{10}

10^{9}

10^{8}

THE CREATIVE
DESTRUCTION
OF EVOLUTION

10^{7}

10^{6}

How complexity takes a simple view on
the dynamics of the new

10^{5}

The work of economist Joseph Schumpeter could help us
understand the transition periods of evolution that drive
innovation and are currently not explained by Darwinian theory.

10^{4}

10^{3}

......

Stefan Thurner

10^{2}

10^{1}

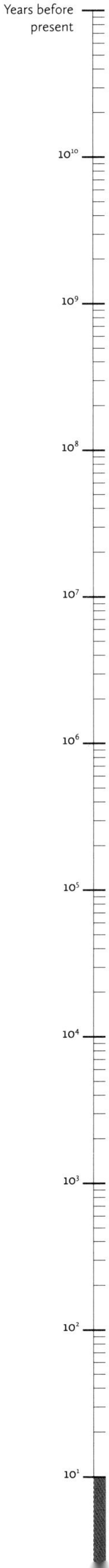

At our present moment in history, we know a great deal about how our universe began and how life evolved. We now know that evolution is a universal phenomenon that applies not only to biology but also to society, the economy and almost every complex adaptive system known to mankind. But for all our recent advances, we still have much more to learn about evolution, how it progresses in the way that it does and how it might behave in the future.

What we do know is that evolution usually happens gradually, but from time to time breaks out disruptively, resulting in booms, busts, bubbles, mass extinctions and subsequent diversification. These periods of stability interspersed with rapid

> My own personal hero, when it comes to answering questions about evolution, is a rather suspicious-looking Austrian gentleman by the name of Joseph Schumpeter.

transitions are known as punctuated equilibria, a term first coined by biologists in the 1960s. Though we now have well-developed theories from evolutionary biology about the stable states, we don't have an equivalent explanation for the transitions, the crazy periods where things are trying to re-establish themselves and where it is not clear where the next equilibrium will end up.

These transitions matter tremendously, but a Darwinian understanding of evolution does not account for them. We have been thinking about evolution for 150 years now and we still do not understand these transitions. We don't understand why they exist, their amplitudes, how often they occur, the durations of the restructuring periods and so on. With the help of concepts from complexity science, however, we are slowly beginning to chip away at our ignorance.

A SIMPLER VIEW OF EVOLUTION

My own personal hero, when it comes to answering questions about evolution, is a rather suspicious-looking Austrian gentleman by the name of Joseph Schumpeter. Schumpeter was a revolutionary in the sense that he understood that the economy evolves in bursts that he called 'gales of destruction'.

Unlike the traditional view of evolutionary dynamics which says that new species come about when they find and fill an unoccupied ecological niche, Schumpeter proposed a process called 'creative destruction', where new things become so successful that they drive out and destroy existing things.

The niche-filling model is captured by the replicator equation, which connects the rate of change of the numbers of a species to its fitness for a given niche. The replicator equation is very good at explaining population dynamics at the equilibria, but does a poor job of explaining the transitions. It is a very simple view of evolution, but has nonetheless become the dominant theory. Stripping away the assumption of the existence of niches, I propose an even simpler view.

PAGE 210
A new sprout after a forest fire.

OPPOSITE
Joseph Schumpeter in 1943.

......

REALITY, DISRUPTED

At a fundamental level, any novelty that is a precondition of evolution arises from the combination of pre-existing things—goods, services, species, methods, ideas and so on. There are rules determining how different things can be combined. For example, there is a rule that if I combine oxygen and hydrogen, I get water. But there is no rule that if I combine a fish and a chicken I will get a dog; the probability of that occurring is zero.

> Schumpeter proposed a process called 'creative destruction', where new things become so successful that they drive out and destroy existing things.

Whether or not we know what these rules are is irrelevant; the rule that oxygen and hydrogen gives water existed long before we understood it. However, the rules only apply if the prerequisite ingredients are present in the system. For example, glass plus electronics gives us a smartphone, but smartphones could not exist in the past when the electronics required had not been invented, even though glass was already around. Reality, then, is made up of rules plus the things that are actually present.

Let's now assume that from time to time—say, once every million time steps—something completely different that does not require anything else comes into existence: a falling meteor brings a new element onto the planet, for example. Or, conversely, a pre-existing thing randomly becomes destroyed by external forces: an endangered species goes extinct, perhaps.

Amazingly, when we assume a random set of these simple rules and a small initial population of things, and feed this into a computer simulation, we reproduce the punctuated equilibria that we observe in nature. For long stretches of time, the same set of things exists. From time to time we have disruptive periods, after which the world is different: a new set of things has formed and will stick around for a while. If we analyse the frequency and strengths of these transitions, we get power law distributions, which is exactly what is seen in mass extinction events, fluctuations in commodity prices, innovation dynamics and other complex systems.

INTRODUCING A SELECTION MECHANISM

Over the last decade, my colleagues and I have generated many variants of this model, changing the networks, how entities are created and destroyed, and, importantly, imposing limits on the levels of resources available. However, all these model modifications were irrelevant: the same dynamics come out every time. This behaviour sometimes happens in physics when you find a phenomenon that is universal—the details do not affect the outcome.

And yet what I have described so far is not yet a full-fledged theory; it merely describes the creative part of evolution. In describing and explaining evolution, the selection mechanism is a very important component. To add selection to our simple model, we introduced another set of rules that specify the removal of existing things when two entities combine. These new rules capture Schumpeter's idea of creative destruction, as seen in the example of how the combination of the combustion engine with wheels drove out the horse carriage industry.

> Starting out with an initial set of creative and destructive rules, new objects come into existence while old ones are removed.

Starting out with an initial set of creative and destructive rules, new objects come into existence while old ones are removed. If we repeat this process again and again, we find that the dynamics are those of a self-organised critical system, like a sand pile whose slope grows as individual grains are added, but then suddenly avalanches go off and the slope becomes flatter. After that the slope increases again—the angle of the slope self-organises around a critical slope.

We found that as the number of rules governing creative combinations increased, the diversity of the system gradually began

to increase, with more objects becoming possible. However, once a critical mass was reached, adding a single new object caused an abruptly new situation, giving rise to a highly diverse environment. On the flipside, this type of critical behaviour also works in the opposite direction. This implies that in a highly diversified environment such as our biosphere, the removal of a single species could trigger a transition to a completely collapsed phase.

DARWIN OR SCHUMPETER?

Because our model involves creating new entities through combination and depends on an underlying evolutionary network, we call it the combinatorial, co-evolutionary critical model, or CCC model for short. By comparing our CCC model with real data, we can finally address the question of whether evolution does indeed follow Darwinian niche-filling or if Schumpeter's mechanism of creative destruction applies.

World trade data, which shows us which country is shipping which products at what price, was a good data set to test our model on. To make any of the 5,000 product classes that are being shipped around the world, people with the necessary skills are required. However, not all countries have all the skills required to make all the available goods within their own borders. These countries then have to buy those goods from other countries, and all these transactions are captured in the data.

> We can finally address the question of whether evolution does indeed follow Darwinian niche-filling or if Schumpeter's mechanism of creative destruction applies.

In our model, the things that are being combined are skills. For instance, one skill could be your ability to read, which, when combined with a teacher, enables you to become a creative scientist who then produces a product. When we fixed the initial conditions of the model to the data in 1984 and let the model evolve over time,

In our model, the things that are being combined are skills.

we were able to accurately predict the diversity of goods available in individual countries 20 years later.

Based on our model, we invented an index that we named the Schumpeterian product index. If the index is positive, then new industries push out old ones through creative destruction. A negative index, on the other hand, implies that new industries are created when companies go out of business, leaving business opportunities that others manage to find and fill.

When we plotted the distribution of each country's Schumpeterian product index, we saw that the curve is not centred exactly around zero, but is shifted to the right. Though the degree is modest, it is nonetheless a significant indication that what is happening with world trade data is Schumpeterian creative destruction rather than Darwinian niche-filling.

A UNIVERSAL DYNAMIC?

Apart from world trade data, we have also tested our model against data on the number of species captured in the fossil record over the last 500 million years, the rates of chemical reactions happening in *Escherichia coli* bacteria, and GDP statistics over time. In each case, we found that our predictions fit the empirical data extremely well, which is amazing considering the range of data covered and the relative simplicity of our model.

Through complexity research such as ours, we are now making modest progress towards understanding the distribution of evolutionary transitions, how big the steps are, how long transitory periods are on average and how 'bursty' they are. All these parameters can be computed from the statistics of our CCC model. While we certainly do not claim to be able to predict the future of evolution, we are taking a small step towards understanding the systemic impact of risks on complex systems from biology to economics.

Stefan Thurner *is a professor at the Medical University of Vienna, Austria, where he chairs the Section for Science of Complex Systems. He is also an external professor at the Santa Fe Institute, a senior researcher at the International Institute for Applied Systems Analysis and president of the Complexity Science Hub.*

This chapter is based on 'Why It Could Make Sense to Understand How Evolution Works—Finally—After 10¹⁰ Years', a talk given by Stefan Thurner on 20 November 2017 in Singapore as part of the *10-on-10: The Chronicles of Evolution* lecture series. The material here was abstracted and edited by Rebecca Tan.

FURTHER READING

Klimek et al. (2009) Evolutionary dynamics from a variational principle. *Physical Review E.* 10.1103/PhysRevE.82.011901

Klimek et al. (2009) Pruning the tree of life: k-core percolation as selection mechanism. *Journal of Theoretical Biology.* 10.1016/j.jtbi.2008.09.030

Thurner and Hanel (2010) Physics of evolution: Selection without fitness. *Physica A: Statistical Mechanics and its Applications.* 10.1016/j.physa.2009.10.030

Thurner et al. (2010) Schumpeterian economic dynamics as a quantifiable model of evolution. *New Journal of Physics.* 10.1088/1367-2630/12/7/075029

Klimek et al. (2012) Empirical confirmation of creative destruction from world trade data. *PLOS One.* 10.1371/journal.pone.0038924

Chapter 20

10^{10}

10^{9}

10^{8}

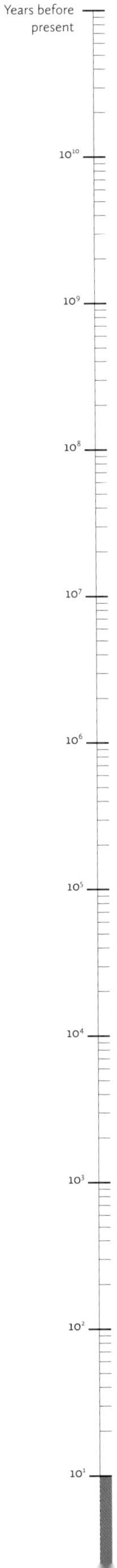

THE CHALLENGE OF THE

10^{7}

ANTHROPOCENE

10^{6}

10^{5}

Approaching planet Earth's tipping point

Multiple indicators suggest that we are in a new geological age
where the actions of human beings are destabilising the planet.

10^{4}

10^{3}

J. Stephen Lansing

10^{2}

10^{1}

Over the past 4.5 billion years, the state of the Earth has largely been determined by planetary and geological dynamics. When massive volcanoes erupted 252 million years ago, it triggered the Great Dying, a mass extinction event that wiped out 96 percent of all marine life and 70 percent of all vertebrates on land. Similarly, when a giant asteroid hit the Earth 66 million years ago, catastrophic changes in climate brought an end to the era of the dinosaurs.

Each of these major transitions has made its mark on the Earth, leaving behind a measurable trace that scientists now use as an indicator of a distinct geological age. Although geologists are still debating what a suitable indicator for our present age would be, there is growing consensus that the arrival of humankind has ushered in a period of unprecedented change—a new epoch called the Anthropocene. Unlike every epoch, era or eon before it, the Anthropocene's climate and environment are thought to be predominantly influenced by human activity.

> Unlike every epoch, era or eon before it, the Anthropocene's climate and environment are thought to be predominantly influenced by human activity.

THE RISE OF HUMANKIND

Early humans first evolved during the Pleistocene, an epoch commonly known as the last Ice Age. Back then, the human population was very small, numbering an estimated 10,000 to 20,000 individuals; their collective impact on the environment was close to negligible in the grand scheme of things.

But as the climate warmed during the subsequent epoch, called the Holocene, a favourable environment and abundant food allowed humans to flourish. While it took 300,000 years for the human population to reach its first billion, adding the next billion took only about 100 years. The population is now an estimated seven billion strong, after the addition of another billion people just over the span of the past 12 years. Alongside the sheer growth in numbers during the Holocene, humans also began developing culture—new ways of living together in cities—and the ability to bend the environment to our needs with agriculture.

When we ask ourselves why all these changes only happened in the last 12,000 years rather than during the Pleistocene, when humans were presumably just as intelligent, the usual answer is that the climate was stable during the Holocene, and it was an extremely agreeable period of time in which to become a farmer. As we find ourselves at the advent of the Anthropocene, however, the question is whether we can expect continued stability or whether a tipping point is imminent.

PAGE 220
Aerial view of the city of Hong Kong.

......

LESSONS FROM DAISYWORLD

When we go back even further in time, we see that the temperature on Earth has remained remarkably stable over the last three billion years, despite the fact that the Sun has become about 30 percent warmer over the same period of time. In contrast, the temperature on Mars has increased, tracking the increasing luminosity of the Sun. Venus once had an Earth-like atmosphere, but in effect experienced a runaway greenhouse effect which caused its surface water to evaporate into the atmosphere, leaving it extremely hot and unconducive to life as we know it.

The question of what makes Earth so uniquely hospitable to life is a hugely complicated one, so it is perhaps easier to understand if we simplify the problem. Daisyworld, a model proposed by scientist James Lovelock in the 1980s, is probably the simplest model that tries to answer that question.

Daisyworld is an imaginary planet identical to Earth, circling a sun that is identical to our Sun. The only difference is that only two living things grow on Daisyworld: black daisies and white daisies. As we move through time from the older, cooler sun to the present hotter one, the temperature on Daisyworld should track the increasing luminosity of its sun. Instead, the flowers have a stabilising effect and hold the temperature constant up until a certain point.

How it works is that the black daisies absorb a little more
heat than the white ones, acquiring a selective advantage when
Daisyworld is cold. Gradually, the black daisies begin to outcompete the white ones and eventually change the reflectance or
albedo of the whole planet. Daisyworld thus becomes darker and
warmer, until it crosses a threshold where the sun heats the planet
to the point beyond the optimum for daisy growth. At that point,
the remaining white daisies have a selective advantage because they
reflect heat and are able to grow faster. By simple natural selection,

the white daisies start to take over and once again change Daisyworld's albedo, thereby stabilising the temperature.

However, the temperature of the sun eventually rises to the point where it becomes too hot even for the white daisies. At this point, all the daisies die and the feedback relationship maintaining the stable temperature breaks down.

Daisyworld is an imaginary planet identical to Earth, circling a sun that is identical to our Sun. The only difference is that only two living things grow on Daisyworld: black daisies and white daisies.

SIGNS OF A NEW AGE

For our own planet, the point of no return—where the Sun becomes so hot that the oceans completely evaporate—is about a billion years away. But there is reason to believe that the Anthropocene could bring this date forward to well within our children's lifetimes.

Imagine if an opportunistic entrepreneur arrives on Daisyworld and decides that the planet has great potential for the interstellar flower trade. He then initiates massive harvesting of daisies, but in the process removes so many that the feedback relationship maintaining the temperature of Daisyworld is destroyed. We would then have a tipping point and phase transition, and Daisyworld would become extremely hot.

Are there similar limits to human activity on planet Earth, beyond which it will be impossible for us to survive? These tipping points involve non-linear changes, known to ecologists as regime shifts, where the effects are not proportionate to the cause. On measures such as temperature, the oceans, urban growth and even plastic, all signs point towards an accelerating rate of change, suggesting that a tipping point is on the horizon.

One strange possible tipping point is plastic. Under business-as-usual, the ocean is expected to contain more plastic than fish by

2050, with untold effects on the fish themselves and the humans who eat them. Plastic aside, there is new evidence that there could be a slowdown in the global meridional circulation, the ocean's great conveyor belt that is responsible for moving heat and nutrients on a planetary scale.

Even if the global meridional circulation does not come grinding to a halt, the rapid increase in urbanisation might represent another tipping point. In 2014, the G20 nations agreed to invest US$70 trillion in new infrastructure by 2030, which translates into 25 million more kilometres of roads and hundreds more dams, 90 percent of which will be built in the tropics. According to ecologist William Laurance, the environmental effects of this infrastructure tsunami could easily dwarf the impacts of climate change and the acidification of the oceans.

RISING TO THE CHALLENGE

How much plastic can the oceans absorb, and how much ecological damage can the Earth sustain? What are the boundary conditions within which a safe, stable human society is possible? We have estimates but we do not have the answers. The more we understand about environmental impact, however, the more we realise how even the best of human intentions can have disastrous and unintended outcomes.

In my research on rice farming on the volcanic island of Bali, Indonesia, for example, we have discovered that the Green Revolution disrupted hundreds of years of tradition that had hitherto been sustained through a self-organised network of water temples. Although practices introduced during the Green Revolution—the use of fertilisers and multiple cropping, for instance—have been credited with helping to meet the needs of a growing human population, such practices were counterproductive in Bali, which has mineral-rich volcanic soil and a carefully balanced system of irrigation. Using fertilisers was not only unnecessary, but in fact created downstream

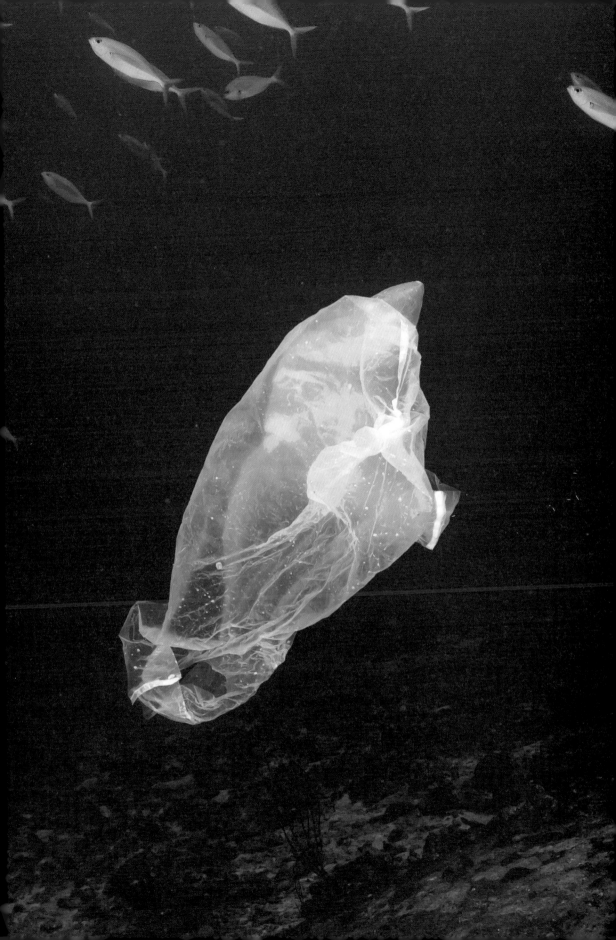

> There is a time lag between society's ability to recognise the magnitude of these problems and the possibilities for mitigation.

problems when the fertiliser-laden runoff caused algal blooms that killed the surrounding coral reefs.

My conclusion is that such problems have snuck up on us. Subsidising fertiliser with the goal of helping the country feed itself was not a bad idea; the plan backfired because it did not include provisions for carefully measuring the quantities of fertiliser that were needed. We need to be more sensitive to adjusting the levels of chemicals or materials that we are putting into the environment, be it nitrogen fertilisers, carbon dioxide or plastic.

There is a time lag between society's ability to recognise the magnitude of these problems and the possibilities for mitigation. Many of the environmental problems we face can technically be solved; what is hindering us is more a matter of political will. We know the alternatives to fossil fuels, plastics and so on, but our trailing ability to steer global governance is in a race with the rapidly advancing consequences of our actions.

That is not to say that all is lost. We do have an example of successful innovation in the Montreal Protocol, an international agreement to phase out ozone-depleting chemicals. Although the problem of ozone depletion was initially dismissed by industry players, rigorous scientific evidence eventually convinced the world to recognise the problem and act decisively, making the Montreal Protocol the world's first universally ratified treaty. The banning of ozone-depleting chemicals thus represents the expansion of our steering capacity and the possibilities of good governance, a rare sign of hope in the age of the Anthropocene.

J. Stephen Lansing *is director of the Complexity Institute and*
a professor at the Asian School of the Environment at Nanyang
Technological University, Singapore. He is also an external professor
at the Santa Fe Institute and the Vienna Complexity Hub, an emeritus
professor of anthropology at the University of Arizona, and a senior
research fellow at the Stockholm Resilience Centre.

This chapter is based on 'The Challenge of the Anthropocene', a talk given by J. Stephen Lansing on
18 September 2017 in Singapore as part of the *10-on-10: The Chronicles of Evolution* lecture series.
The material here was abstracted and edited by Rebecca Tan.

FURTHER READING

Lansing (1991) *Priests and programmers: technologies of power in the engineered landscape of Bali.*
Princeton: Princeton University Press.

Lansing et al. (1998) System-dependent selection, ecological feedback and the emergence of
functional structure in ecosystems. *Journal of Theoretical Biology.* 10.1006/jtbi.1998.0664

Lansing (2006) *Perfect order: recognizing complexity in Bali.* Princeton: Princeton University Press.

Lansing et al. (2017) Adaptive self-organization of Bali's ancient rice terraces. *Proceedings of the
National Academy of Sciences of the United States of America.* doi: 10.1073/pnas.1605369114

Chapter 21

DIFFICULT QUESTIONS IN EVOLUTION

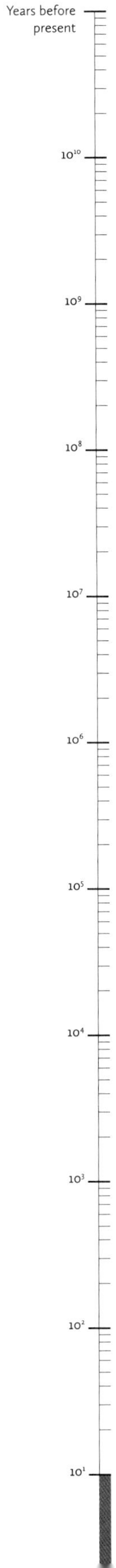

Years before present
10^{10}
10^{9}
10^{8}
10^{7}
10^{6}
10^{5}
10^{4}
10^{3}
10^{2}
10^{1}

The power of evolutionary thinking

Even though Darwin's theory of evolution is a simple concept at its core, evolutionary reasoning can help us make sense of the biggest questions in science, from the origin of life to the workings of the human brain.

Eörs Szathmáry

For an idea that holds so much power, Darwin's theory of evolution can be summarised in remarkably few words: in a population of multiplying organisms, variation exists in the hereditary traits that are passed from parent to offspring; if this variation affects the ability of organisms to survive or reproduce, then natural selection can occur.

Those are the basics. Of course, you could then go on to ask many more questions that require deeper analysis. Consider Newton's laws—they are simple and elegant, but if you want to use them to work out whether a bridge will collapse or not, your calculations could run into pages and pages. The same is true of evolutionary theory.

In this chapter, we are going to consider some of the most burning and difficult questions in evolution. In the process, we will see some very interesting cases of evolutionary reasoning, where I hope its real power will unfold.

······

EIGEN'S PARADOX AND THE ORIGIN OF LIFE

The first difficult question concerns the origin of life—how complex organisms evolved from simple molecules on the early Earth.

Unlike DNA today, the earliest replicators—molecules that carry genetic information and copy themselves—did not have cellular enzymes to repair copying errors; as a result, they were riddled with mutations. The Nobel laureate and physical chemist Manfred Eigen worked out in 1971 that without a repair mechanism, the longest stretch of genetic material that can be reliably copied (before runaway mutation destroys the message) is only about 100 nucleotides, much too short to encode repair enzymes and other complex proteins. Even if a genome were to be composed of multiple such short stretches, the faster-replicating stretches would eventually outcompete the slower ones, which would then be lost.

Eigen's paradox poses a chicken-and-egg problem for the origin of life—accurate replication requires longer stretches of genetic information, but longer stretches of genetic information in turn require accurate replication. Eigen himself proposed an ingenious resolution: the molecular hypercycle, a 'cycle of cycles' in which replicators not only catalyse their own formation, but are linked in a cycle such that they also catalyse each other's formation.

While the hypercycle increases the information content the system can carry, it is only stable if all its members play fair. However, as evolutionary biologist John Maynard Smith pointed out in 1979, it is perfectly possible for molecular 'parasites' to arise in the network. Just as tax evaders avail themselves of public goods but do not contribute their part to society, these freeloading mutants accept the catalytic aid of other molecules in the hypercycle but fail to provide it in return. A parasitic takeover can thus short-circuit the hypercycle, causing it to collapse.

> Just as tax evaders avail themselves of public goods but do not contribute their part to society, these freeloading mutants accept the catalytic aid of other molecules in the hypercycle but fail to provide it in return.

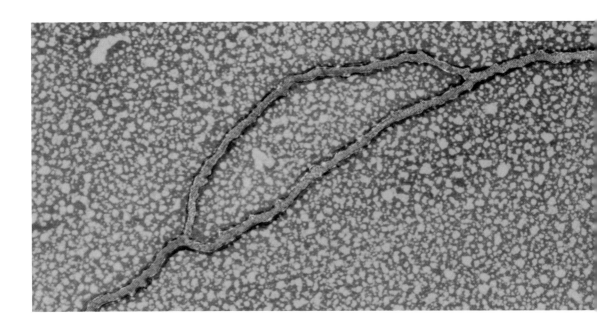

COEXISTING WITH PARASITES

Evolutionary biologists have come up with other solutions to Eigen's paradox that accommodate the appearance of parasites. In David Sloan Wilson's 1980 trait-group selection model, replicators undergo transient compartmentalisation, alternating between mixing in a global pool and being randomly distributed across small niches (crevices in porous rock, for instance). According to the model, this process allows selection to occur at the level of the compartment, resulting in a stable equilibrium between parasites and non-parasites.

Mathematical models of evolution are greatly strengthened by experimental evidence. My collaborators and I recently recreated the trait-group selection model in the laboratory by compartmentalising replicating RNA molecules in tiny droplets of water, selecting for droplets with functional replicators and releasing them back into a global pool. We found that multiple rounds of transient compartmentalisation and selection indeed prevented parasites—in this case, shorter, incomplete RNA molecules—from taking over the system. On the early Earth, a similar process could have helped expand the information content of the first replicators, allowing life to gain a critical toehold.

We would never know whether an evolutionary process works or not unless we buckle down and do the mathematical modelling, and subsequently, attempt to generate experimental evidence.

Eventually, instead of simply being washed in and out of rock crevices, replicators would become enclosed in primitive cells called protocells, which reproduce by dividing. Can Eigen's paradox still be resolved in this scenario? A model I proposed in 1987, called the stochastic corrector model, shows that it can. When a protocell divides, the replicator molecules it contains become randomly distributed between its daughter cells, which therefore vary in replicator composition and hence fitness. The model shows that selection at the level of the protocell favours those with a balanced, optimal composition of replicators, thus preventing parasites from taking over.

An important message here is that although we could speculate endlessly, we would never know whether an evolutionary process works or not unless we buckle down and do the mathematical modelling, and subsequently, attempt to generate experimental evidence. The latter can be quite difficult, and the stochastic corrector model has yet to be implemented in the laboratory.

THE IMPORTANCE OF BEING MODULAR

While living things are subject to evolutionary processes, not all organisms have the same potential for evolutionary change. The next difficult question we will explore is the relatively new concept of evolvability—how good a biological system is at generating adaptive solutions to changing environments. Many factors can impact how evolvable an organism is, but let's focus on one: modularity.

Imagine an organism whose every gene influences many different traits. A single gene could impact eyesight, the length of its big toe, its ability to digest food and so on. Such a non-modular creature would be unevolvable, because any genetic novelty it generates would inevitably result in negative side effects in other traits. By contrast, an organism with genes organised in relatively independent modules, each specialising in a different function, would be much more tolerant of adaptive change.

Consider an iconic example of evolutionary adaptation: Darwin's finches, which display an array of distinct beak shapes associated with their diets. Nectar-sipping finches, for instance, have long, narrow beaks for reaching deep into flowers, while seed-munching finches have short, broad beaks with which to crush their food. These adaptations, it turns out, are underpinned by modularity. Beak length and depth are regulated by two independent genetic pathways, such that each trait can be adjusted independently with little interference on the other; the two traits can thus be combined in any number of ways to define each beak's distinct dimensions.

......

THE EVOLUTION OF EVOLVABILITY

Darwin's finches are just one example of the capacity of organisms to generate novel traits. But how does this evolvability itself evolve? To investigate this in a simple model system, researchers at the Weizmann Institute of Science in Israel used computer simulations to evolve RNA molecules into various shapes, which are composed of structural modules such as hairpin loops and bulges.

In the simulations, the researchers first exposed RNA molecules to selection for a range of different structural modules. After this process, they found that the RNA molecules could evolve into new shapes much more quickly, as long as these shapes consisted of modules previously encountered during the selection regime.

It turned out that the RNA molecules had evolved genetic 'triggers'—strategic positions in a molecule at which small changes can have large structural consequences. Just as a master switch can flip all the lights in a house on or off, a single mutation at a trigger position can result in the appearance or disappearance of an entire module, such as a hairpin loop, thus allowing the molecule to turn on a dime once the environment changes.

That the RNA molecules can retain the memory of previous environments and generalise to novel conditions is an amazing phenomenon. Further study of the mechanisms behind this evolutionary 'learning' is of critical importance, and leads us into new territory, uncharted by Darwin's original theories.

......

DARWIN AND THE BRAIN

Now that we know something about learning in evolution, I would like to turn the tables a little bit and talk about evolution in learning— our final difficult question.

Despite the advent of supercomputers and deep learning algorithms, the human brain remains unrivalled in its ability to

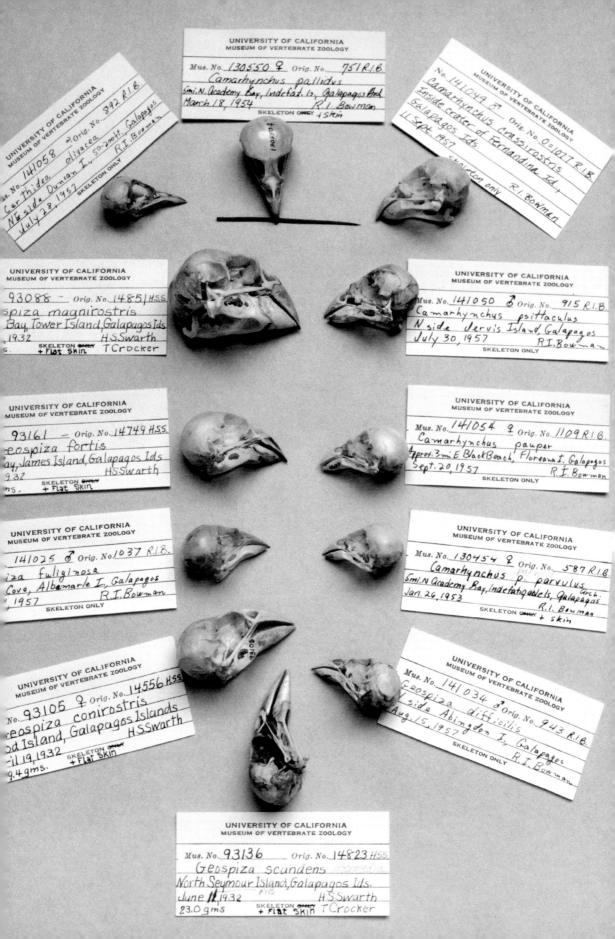

perform complex cognitive tasks, such as learning a language or developing big ideas like Einstein's theory of relativity. One of the most exciting research projects I now work on involves understanding how Darwinian evolutionary processes may underlie and hence explain human cognition.

The notion that selection happens in the brain is not new. In 1973, Jean-Pierre Changeux proposed that organisms start out with surplus neurons and connections, which are then selectively pruned during development—a theory that today has garnered substantial experimental support. But this single round of pruning, even if it occurs over several years, cannot account for complex cognition, as it limits organisms to the neural configuration they end up with.

My colleagues and I have built models that suggest that cognition goes significantly beyond a one-shot process, and instead more closely resembles Darwinian evolution, where variant connections are generated and selected for over multiple iterations. In the brain, this breeding of ideas would happen in massively parallel fashion and on a timescale of milliseconds, giving us plenty of opportunities for iteration in real time.

We are now working on using simulations and laboratory experiments to confirm if this powerful evolutionary search process indeed happens in nature. If so, it would be an incredibly important finding, but also just one of many examples of how Darwinian logic, at 160 years old, can still provide fresh insights into the biggest questions in science.

Despite the advent of supercomputers and deep learning algorithms, the human brain remains unrivalled in its ability to perform complex cognitive tasks, such as learning a language or developing big ideas like Einstein's theory of relativity.

Eörs Szathmáry *is director of the Parmenides Centre for the*
Conceptual Foundations of Science in Pullach, Germany, and professor
of biology at Eötvös Loránd University in Budapest, Hungary. His
main interest is theoretical evolutionary biology, and his work focuses
on the common principles of the major steps in evolution, such as the
origin of life, the emergence of cells, the origin of animal societies and
the appearance of human language. He is a member of the Academia
Europaea and the Hungarian Academy of Sciences.

This chapter is based on 'Difficult Questions in Evolution', a talk given by Eörs Szathmáry on
11 December 2017 in Singapore as part of the *10-on-10: The Chronicles of Evolution* lecture series.
The material here was abstracted and edited by Shuzhen Sim.

FURTHER READING

Szathmáry and Demeter (1987) Group selection of early replicators and the origin of life. *Journal of Theoretical Biology*. 10.1016/S0022-5193(87)80191-1

Parter et al. (2008) Facilitated variation: how evolution learns from past environments to generalize to new environments. *PLoS Computational Biology*. 10.1371/journal.pcbi.1000206

Szathmáry (2015) Toward major evolutionary transitions theory 2.0. *Proceedings of the National Academy of Sciences of the United States of America*. 10.1073/pnas.1421398112

Watson and Szathmáry (2015) How can evolution learn? *Trends in Ecology and Evolution*. 10.1016/j.tree.2015.11.009

Matsumura et al. (2016) Transient compartmentalization of RNA replicators prevents extinction due to parasites. *Science*. 10.1126/science.aag1582

Szilágyi et al. (2016) Breeding novel solutions in the brain: a model of Darwinian neurodynamics. *F1000Research*. 10.12688/f1000research.9630.2

Years before
present

10^{10}

10^9

10^8

10^7

10^6

10^5

10^4

10^3

10^2

10^1

Chapter 22

AN EVOLVING VIEW
ON EVOLUTION

Towards an extended evolutionary synthesis

At 80 years old, standard evolutionary theory needs an upgrade:
a broader, more inclusive framework that will allow it to keep
pace with rapid advances in other fields of biology.

Gerd B. Müller

When Charles Darwin published *On the Origin of Species* in 1859, he did not know what a gene was. Evolutionary theory as we know it today, with its emphasis on genetic variation and inheritance, was forged in the 1930s and 1940s by leading thinkers in the field, who combined Darwinian natural selection with Mendelian inheritance and concepts from population genetics, palaeontology and other disciplines.

In the 80 years or so since this fusion, known as the 'modern synthesis', the biological sciences have seen significant advances. New fields such as molecular genetics, evolutionary developmental biology ('evo-devo') and systems biology, together with new concepts such as modes of inheritance that go beyond genetics, have greatly expanded what we know about the mechanisms of evolutionary change.

These new insights have sparked much debate about whether there is a need to expand or rethink certain aspects of textbook evolutionary theory. In my opinion, the answer is yes—we need a broader framework into which these newly recognised drivers of evolution can be incorporated. After all, theories are never complete; they have always evolved, and the theory of evolution is no exception.

The field of evo-devo, among other questions, investigates how organisms' physical development influences evolutionary processes.

LESSONS FROM EVO-DEVO

In the modern synthesis, genes are the key players. Random mutation gives rise to the genetic variation seen in populations, genetic inheritance alone accounts for the transmission of traits from one generation to the next, and natural selection on these genetically determined traits drives adaptation to environmental and functional demands.

This gene-centric view, while valid within its confined scope, is insufficient to account for the full range of processes that drive evolution—a gap particularly well illustrated by the field of evo-devo, which, among other questions, investigates how organisms' physical

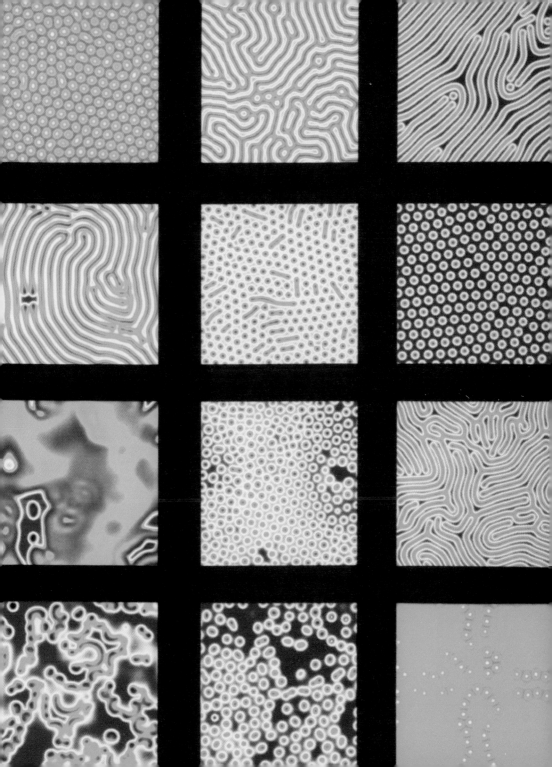

development influences evolutionary processes. The following three evo-devo principles are proving particularly difficult to reconcile with the standard theory.

First, not all variation arises with equal probability— developmental processes have a tendency to generate certain variants more readily than others, a phenomenon known as developmental bias. Every one of the more than 3,000 species of centipedes, for example, has a body that consists of an odd number of leg-bearing segments; that even numbers are not seen is most likely due to constraints imposed by how the segments develop.

BELOW

All centipedes have bodies with an odd number of leg-bearing segments.

Similar constraints are observed in the variation of colour patterns on butterfly wings or digit variation in vertebrates.

Second, while the modern synthesis holds that the minute changes effected by individual genes should render variation gradual and continuous, work from evo-devo tells us that developmental variation can also result from highly discontinuous or bistable mechanisms. For example, during the formation of somites (serial tissue blocks in vertebrate embryos), cells abruptly switch between different developmental states, depending on the molecular environment they are exposed to at their physical location.

> Stripes on a zebrafish, colour patterns on a butterfly's wing, spots on a leopard and many other patterns in nature are not dictated by a strict genetic programme.

The third important evo-devo principle is that not all developmental variation is deterministic. For example, stripes on a zebrafish, colour patches on a butterfly's wing, spots on a leopard and many other patterns in nature are not dictated by a strict genetic programme. Instead, they are produced by diffusing signalling molecules, known as morphogens, which guide approximate cellular behaviours. This type of 'emergent cell patterning', in which structural motifs result from a spatially inhomogeneous mix of morphogens, was first proposed by Alan Turing in 1952.

OUT ON A LIMB

An excellent illustration of these three principles in action comes from polydactylous vertebrates. Maine Coon cats studied by our research group, for instance, frequently have more than the usual 5-5-4-4 (five digits on each forepaw and four on each hindpaw) complement of digits on their limbs.

Polydactyly in these cats is often caused by what is termed the Hemingway mutation—so named for the frequently many-toed felines that famously inhabit Ernest Hemingway's Florida home. As a result of this single-nucleotide genetic substitution, a key developmental morphogen known as Sonic Hedgehog becomes expressed in regions of the limb bud where it is usually absent, thus triggering the formation of extra digits. Interestingly, this same point mutation can result in a variety of outcomes—the addition of varying numbers of extra digits (up to eight) to a cat's limbs—indicating that digit variation is not fully explained by genetics alone.

More pieces of evidence suggest that polydactyly is influenced by developmental processes. For one, the addition of digits occurs in a biased fashion—some configurations appear more frequently than others, with 6-6-4-4 being the most common. Further, polydactyly in these cats is a discontinuous, all-or-nothing phenomenon, with the preferred appearance of complete digits rather than partial components.

PUZZLING OUT POLYDACTYLY

These features of polydactyly are difficult for a gene-centric theory to explain, but can be accounted for (and indeed predicted) by an evo-devo-based model my colleagues and I developed, which we call the Hemingway model.

According to the model, cells in the limb bud act as bistable switches that flip on or off for cartilage differentiation in response to changes in the concentration of morphogens such as Sonic Hedgehog. Full extra digits are produced when the number of activated limb bud cells exceeds certain thresholds, with different threshold levels resulting in different numbers of extra digits, just like a set of steps.

Depending on the number of cells available, different threshold widths account for the bias towards certain digit configurations. In simulations of this model, normal and polydactylous numbers of digit-like stripes arise through emergent patterning, based on the very same Turing-type process mentioned earlier.

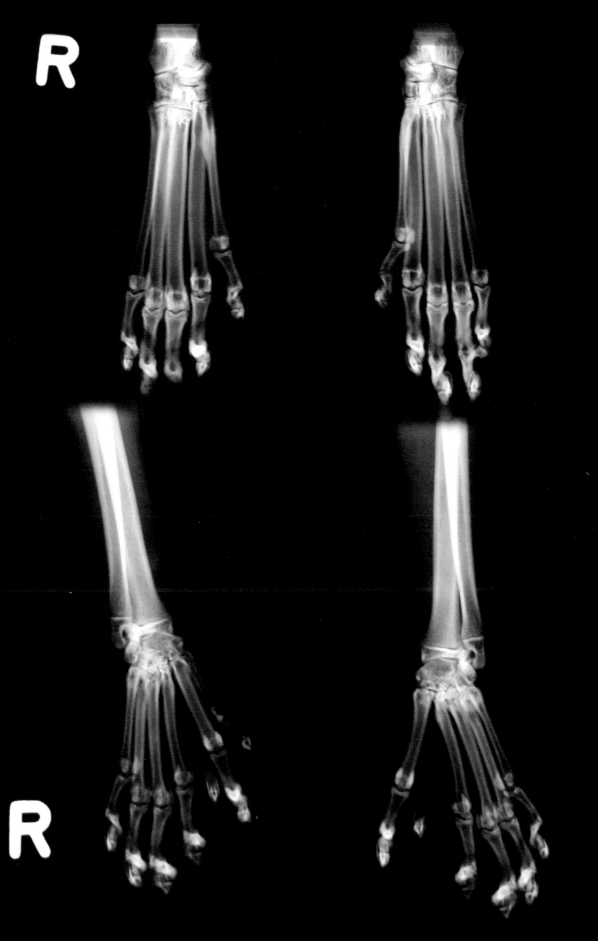

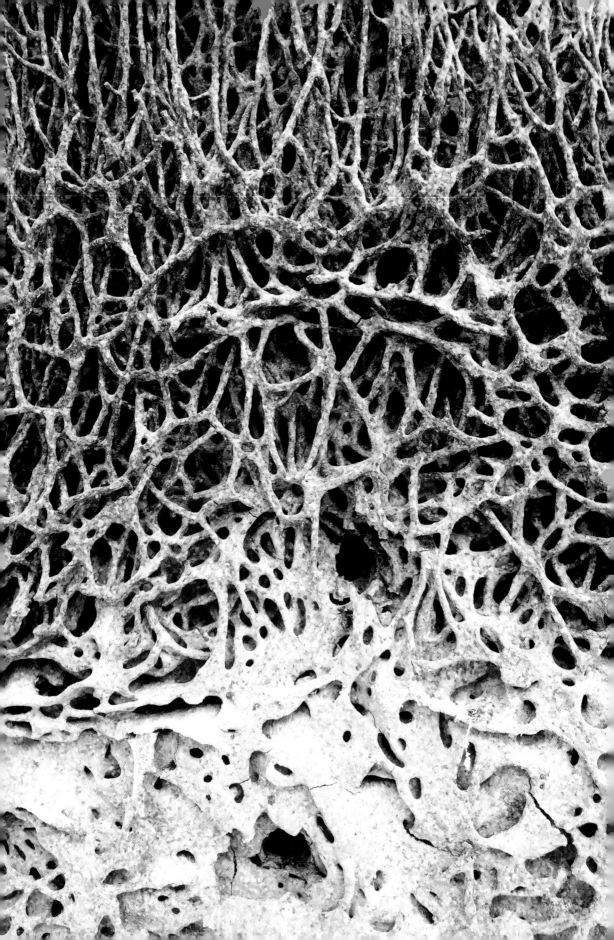

Polydactyly formation is just one of many developmental systems that react in biased, discontinuous and emergent ways, introducing non-linearities into evolutionary processes that the standard theory is hard-pressed to explain, but that evo-devo is very good at predicting.

A DIVERSITY OF CHALLENGES

Alongside evo-devo, new concepts from numerous other fields are likewise challenging standard evolutionary theory. For example, while the modern synthesis is built around genetic inheritance, we now know that selectable traits can also be transmitted through other means, such as epigenetic (where chemical marks, rather than changes in DNA sequence, modify a gene's activity), behavioural and cultural inheritance.

OPPOSITE
Structures like termite nests show that organisms can actively modify their environments.

Another relatively new concept neglected by the classical synthesis is that variation can be induced by direct environmental effects rather than by genetic change—butterfly wings, for instance, may be differently coloured depending on whether the insects emerge in the wet or dry season. Yet, natural selection still acts on this variation, perhaps by maintaining genetic variants that allow developing organisms to respond quickly to environmental perturbations.

At the same time, structures like beaver dams and termite nests remind us that organisms are not merely passive subjects to natural selection, but can also actively modify their environments, which then become the selective environments for subsequent generations. Through this process, known as niche construction, organisms actually co-direct their own evolution by altering their environments and biasing selection—a phenomenon unaccounted for by the traditional view.

> Structures like beaver dams and termite nests remind us that organisms are not merely passive subjects to natural selection, but can also actively modify their environments.

......

EVOLUTION: A MORE INCLUSIVE PICTURE

These examples show us that the central tenets of the modern synthesis, while not wrong, can no longer be regarded as complete explanations for evolutionary change. Hence, a more pluralistic theoretical framework is required—what my colleagues and I term the 'extended evolutionary synthesis' or EES—that brings the novel evolutionary concepts together with elements from standard evolutionary theory.

The EES presents a more complex and inclusive picture of the processes at work in evolution. For example, instead of simple variation in the 'gene pool' of a species, the EES considers a 'developmental system pool' that produces variation in a population, whether it is generated through genetic or non-genetic means. Among other important concepts, the extended framework also recognises non-genetic systems of inheritance, the role of the environment in inducing variation, and the impact of niche construction.

I would like to emphasise, however, that the EES is not a completed theoretical framework. It does not contradict Darwinian theory, but results in a significantly different set of testable predictions than those derived from the modern synthesis. Nor is it the idea of just a few people who wish to revolutionise the field. Rather, it is an ongoing project that stems from the abundance of new data and concepts that have arisen independently in multiple areas of biological research.

While more work needs to be done to define and formalise its various components, the EES provides a structure for scientists to address a multitude of evolutionary phenomena that lie beyond the scope of the modern synthesis, including—besides development—complex traits like behaviour, language and cognition, rapid and punctuated events in evolutionary history, and the interaction of genes and culture. This is indeed an exciting time for evolutionary biology.

Gerd B. Müller *is a professor at the University of Vienna, Austria,*
where he heads the Department of Theoretical Biology. He is president
of the Konrad Lorenz Institute for Evolution and Cognition Research
in Klosterneuburg, Austria, and president of the European Society for
Evolutionary Developmental Biology. His research interests include
developmental pattern formation, evolutionary innovation, evo-devo
and the conceptual advancement of evolutionary theory.

This chapter is based on 'Towards an Extended Evolutionary Synthesis', a talk given by Gerd B.
Müller on 11 December 2017 in Singapore as part of the *10-on-10: The Chronicles of Evolution* lecture
series. The material here was abstracted and edited by Shuzhen Sim.

FURTHER READING

Müller (2007) Evo-devo: Extending the evolutionary synthesis. *Nature Reviews Genetics*.
10.1038/nrg2219

Lange et al. (2014) Biased polyphenism in polydactylous cats carrying a single point mutation:
the Hemingway model for digit novelty. *Evolutionary Biology*. 10.1007/s11692-013-9267-y

Laland et al. (2015) The extended evolutionary synthesis: its structure, assumptions and predictions.
Proceedings of the Royal Society B: Biological Sciences. 10.1098/rspb.2015.1019

Müller (2017) Why an extended evolutionary synthesis is necessary. *Interface Focus*.
10.1098/rsfs.2017.0015

Chapter 23

THE HUMBLE VIEW FROM INSIDE EVOLUTION

The inescapable present and our radically open future

Human beings are the only species able to see evolution from the inside, a view that has implications for how we see the future.

Helga Nowotny

Years before
present

10^{10}

10^9

10^8

10^7

10^6

10^5

10^4

10^3

10^2

10^1

The preceding chapters have traced the course of evolution over millions, thousands and hundreds of years, bringing us now into the present. My claim is that we cannot escape the present, and so should adopt a humble view from inside evolution.

Essentially, the humble view means two things: first, the recognition of the privilege that we are the only species on Earth that has the ability to reflect on evolution and see it from the inside. Second, a humble view from the inside also means that we should reflect on what we are doing in and with evolution. This allows us, or perhaps obliges us, to speculate also about the future of evolution.

THE INESCAPABLE PRESENT

Being in the present means that we know a lot about the past, even the very distant deep past. In 2017, the Nobel Prize in Physics was awarded to three researchers who with hundreds of others were engaged in setting up the Laser Interferometer Gravitational-Wave Observatory (LIGO) experiment to detect gravitational waves, which originated from an event that happened 1.3 billion years ago.

And yet we cannot see what happened 1.3 billion years ago. We can only see representations—computer visualisations or artistic impressions. Through such representations, we are given the feeling that we are experiencing past events as though they were happening now, in the present.

> Every time we look into the past, we are entering into an active dialogue with historical events and people we have never met.

So we are able to look into the past of the universe, but we do it from the present. The same holds for fossils, which have been a wonderful treasure trove of evidence helping us to reconstruct the history of life on Earth, and of course for DNA, the discovery of which 65 years ago showed us how closely related all living things are.

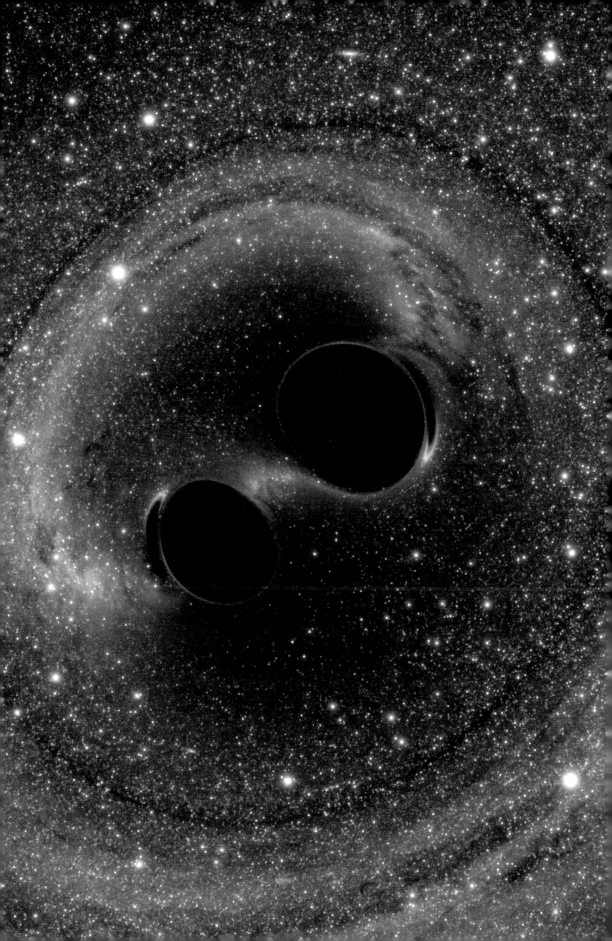

Every time we look into the past, we are entering into an active dialogue with historical events and people we have never met. We can only reconstruct what they did or thought by asking questions of them, and we tend to ask questions related to our present concerns. So we are once again caught in the present, because the questions we ask of history are always questions that have some kind of meaning, importance or relevance to us in the present.

From an evolutionary point of view, humans are unique in terms of the scale at which we have restructured and built our own eco-niches, changing the way the planet functions in the process. The downside of our planetary niche construction is that it is the only niche humans have; we are confronted with the inevitable outcomes of our actions. Once again, there is no escape from the present and the consequences of living in our present age.

AN OPEN FUTURE

Our inability to escape the present also has something to do with the way we approach the future. We are essentially blind about the future, as it does not leave traces as the past does. And yet our blindness about the future exerts, at the same time, an enormous fascination. Reflecting this fascination, we find the practice of divination in almost every ancient culture. In the case of oracle bones from the Shang dynasty, curiosity about the future led to the development of writing.

Today, our practices do not include heating bones over a fire and interpreting the cracks. Instead, we stretch our imaginations through writing reports about what will happen in 2030, 2040, 2050 and so on. We put data in our models and try to guess at what the future will bring. Adopting the humble view from inside evolution means admitting that we are blind towards the future, even as we continue to be fascinated by what it will bring and strive to expand our view of it.

This idea that the future is open is a fairly recent cultural invention, and one that has had a significant impact in the history of human evolution. Until the 18th century, most people believed that the future was predetermined by the gods, fate or other forces of the universe, and all we could do was either pray to the gods to change what they had decided, or resort to other ways of trying to influence what was essentially already pre-set. But in the period between 1750 and 1850, referred to by the German historian Reinhart Koselleck as saddle time, people discovered that their past experience diverged from their expectations. The future could be different from the past. It became an open horizon for new opportunities.

This new way of looking at the future, of seeing it as a wide, open horizon rather than a circular loop, had a lot to do with science and technology. Science enabled humanity to explore the world, manipulate our environment, intervene and change circumstances. What we are discovering about the past—gravitational waves in the universe, our common ancestry through DNA in the living world, and human history—would not be possible without science. Science and technology are thus very much tied to cultural and social evolution.

BELOW
The ancient Greek philosopher and scientist Aristotle proposed a three-fold typology of knowledge: *episteme*, *techne* and *phronesis*.

THREE TYPES OF KNOWLEDGE

Important as science and technology may be, they are not the only types of knowledge that exist. Well before our modern scientific era, Aristotle proposed a three-fold typology of knowledge: *episteme*, *techne* and *phronesis*. *Episteme*, which means 'to know' in Greek, is based on rationality and analogous to scientific knowledge. *Techne*, from which the word 'technology' derives its name, translates to a craft or practice.

Episteme and *techne* are thought of as partners to each other, and are familiar to us as science and technology. But Aristotle had a third, often forgotten, category: *phronesis*, which means practical wisdom. I would argue that *phronesis*, including ethical considerations and deliberations in trying to reach consensus and pragmatic outcomes, has important lessons to teach us as we consider the evolution of science and technology.

The focus—and sometimes even obsession—with technological innovation can make us overlook that there are also social innovations that are just as important. The field of medicine, for example, is undergoing amazing technological disruption. But its full potential cannot unfold without equally innovative changes in how healthcare systems and hospitals are being run. The more technological innovations we want, the more social innovations we need to accompany them. Other social innovations like the rule of law, courts and secret ballots can be thought of as social technologies that are essential for us to live together in a peaceful way.

The point I want to make is that we should not focus on only one type of knowledge, but instead consider how all knowledge is interlinked and embedded in a wider context. The humble view from the inside alerts us to the co-evolution of culture, technology and science.

......

BETWEEN HUBRIS AND HUMILITY

In fact, we are now at a point where cultural evolution has overtaken biological evolution. With new tools in the life sciences, like CRISPR, we are now able to reshape our genomes, edit our DNA and change entire regulatory networks. But this accelerated overtaking of biological evolution also raises new questions, the most urgent of which is how to manage unintentionally induced change.

We are not fully in control of what we are doing, and we may never be. For many people this is a cause of anxiety and fear of the future. These unintentional changes will have different consequences for different parts of the population. While certain developments like

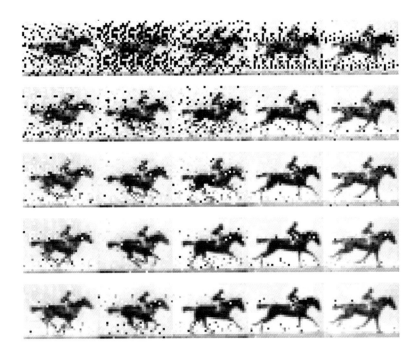

LEFT
Paving the way for DNA to be used as a medium for information storage, researchers encoded this image (from Eadweard Muybridge's *Human and Animal Locomotion* series of photographs) in the genomes of *Escherichia coli* bacteria, and were subsequently able to reconstruct it using DNA sequencing. As the number of DNA sequence reads increases (top to bottom), the number of missing pixels decreases.

artificial intelligence may be beneficial to society as a whole, they may disadvantage those who, for example, lose their jobs to automation and are unable to reinvent themselves.

Beyond technological challenges, we also face planetary limitations, which, as I have discussed earlier, have inescapable consequences. What social innovations are required to enable us to survive these changes?

In fact, we are now at a point where cultural evolution has overtaken biological evolution.

One positive social change is the fact that we are starting to embrace cooperation over competition. People like biochemist and mathematician Martin Nowak have realised that we have downplayed the role of cooperation in evolution. Experiments show that people are willing to help each other even at a cost to themselves, so we are not all narcissists and egomaniacs hell-bent on maximising our own economic benefit. Students are also now being told that working in teams is one of the skills that universities would like to teach them, reflecting an evolution of social norms towards cooperation.

The increasing recognition and acceptance of disabled people and other marginalised groups is another sign that humanity is slowly becoming more inclusive. Yet at the same time, we also see the persistence of racism and other kinds of pernicious behaviour.

This brings us to where we stand at the present, on the cusp of our immediate future. There are many speculations about where we are headed. In all our predictions of what will happen in the future, we will make many miscalculations and miss out on very important developments, because the future continues to be uncertain yet open.

So, we find ourselves firmly poised in our evolutionary present, oscillating between our hubris and humility. Hubris is the over-estimation of our capacity, which has happened throughout history. Hubris also means over-reliance on a single solution, believing that one knows the right solution and relying exclusively on it, be it a technological fix or a purely economic solution that does not take the complexity of societal systems into consideration.

The humble view, however, acknowledges that technology, science and culture evolve together, and that taking a single component out of this co-evolutionary mesh will lead to over-confidence and arrogance. The humble view recognises that life will continue to evolve in unpredictable ways. The process of research is inherently uncertain, but it is through science that we reach out to bring the future into the present.

> We find ourselves firmly poised in our evolutionary present, oscillating between our hubris and humility.

I want to close by recalling the words of Sydney Brenner, who once remarked that mathematics deals with the perfect, physics with the optimal and the life sciences with the satisfactory. He did not mention the social sciences. My message is that the social sciences have to be included if we want to better understand the role played by humans in the ongoing history of evolution, especially in the socio-cultural evolution driven by us. This is why it is left to the social sciences to deal with the messy.

Helga Nowotny *is professor emerita of science and technology studies at ETH Zurich, Switzerland, and a founding member of the European Research Council, of which she was president until 2013. She is currently a visiting professor at Nanyang Technological University, Singapore, a member of the steering board of the Falling Walls Foundation, and chair of the scientific advisory board of the Complexity Science Hub in Vienna, Austria.*

This chapter is based on 'A Humble View from Inside Evolution', a talk given by Helga Nowotny on 20 November 2017 in Singapore as part of the *10-on-10: The Chronicles of Evolution* lecture series. The material here was abstracted and edited by Rebecca Tan.

FURTHER READING

Nowotny (2008) *Insatiable curiosity: innovation in a fragile future* (trans. Cohen). Cambridge: MIT Press.

Nowotny and Testa (2011) *Naked genes: reinventing the human in the molecular age* (trans. Cohen). Cambridge: MIT Press.

Nowotny (2015) *The cunning of uncertainty*. Cambridge: Polity Press.

Nowotny (2017) *An orderly mess*. Budapest and New York: Central European University Press.

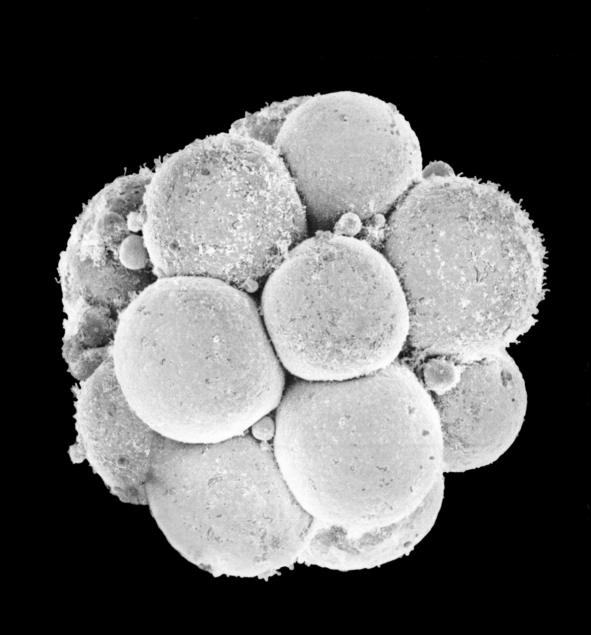

EPILOGUE

Sydney Brenner

Darwin's theory of natural selection has been powerfully strengthened by our understanding of the basic machinery of genetic determination, initiated by James Watson and Francis Crick in 1953 with their model of DNA. The genetical theory of natural selection recognises that it is the genes that exist inside all organisms that will determine the changes in these organisms, all the way from the origin of life to the advent of humans.

If you ask yourself what is the minimum number of genes you need to make a primitive bacterium, the answer appears to be of the order of about 1,800. These genes specify the proteins that synthesise, repair and recombine DNA, and that carry out the catalytic steps for the synthesis of all the components of cells and for their regulation. However, common bacteria such as *Escherichia coli* have more than 4,000 genes. What is *E. coli* doing with these extra 2,000 genes?

ONE ORGANISM, TWO WORLDS

The important feature is that *E. coli* has found a way to live in two worlds. It can live inside animals, as it does in our intestines, and it can also live outside animals, in open environments such as soil and water.

Inside our intestines, *E. coli* can get a lot of food for nothing; it is a parasite. It has constructed regulatory machinery that allows it to turn off the extra genes involved in biosynthesis, and because biosynthesis is very expensive in terms of energy and material requirements, all the resources of the cell

become directed to faster growth and multiplication. The extra genes have
been acquired by transfer from other bacteria.

This takes us back to the genetical theory of natural selection. In order
to evolve, new genes are needed to carry out new functions. They can be
stolen from other organisms, or the whole genome can be duplicated and
new functions selected by mutation or rearrangement.

MAPPING THE HISTORY OF LIFE

We need a framework to understand how complexity is gained in the course
of evolution, and how mutation, which is only a chance effect, eventually
leads to enormous changes in living organisms.

I have over the past 25 years developed a framework to study this question.
The genetic code has a universal structure, and the 64 triplets are assigned
to the 20 amino acids and chain termination in a pattern that is the same for
all organisms. Some amino acids have as many as six synonymous codons.
Thus, identical organisms can be built with markedly different nucleotide
sequences in their genes and expressed messenger RNA.

This allows us to take all organisms that have been sequenced, count the
codons used by them to make their proteins and make maps of their genomes.
In this way, we can study all changes that are independent of selection, and
that are dependent only on the passage of time.

The fundamental property of living organisms is the invention of
computing with DNA. Organisms can be shown to be evolving at different
rates—some are very fast, others, very slow. Some, like the flowering plants,
have reached equilibrium. Inside every genome there is a clock, and it ticks
at a rate that we can measure.

Our main conclusion from studying the history of genomes is that all
the major changes, from prokaryotes to eukaryotes, from unicellular to
multicellular, from water to land, from invertebrates to vertebrates, from
apes to humans, are the products of lucky accidents that could not have been
predicted. Otherwise, only randomness is exploited. This is why evolution
takes so much time and why degeneracy and extinction are so common. This
is also the underlying theme that links the chronicles of evolution.

ABOVE

A map of some 1.7 billion stars in the Milky Way and neighbouring galaxies, based on observations from the European Space Agency's Gaia satellite and displayed in an equirectangular projection. The two bright objects in the lower right of the image are the Large and Small Magellanic Clouds, two dwarf galaxies orbiting the Milky Way.

ABOUT
SYDNEY BRENNER

......

Sydney Brenner was born in 1927 in South Africa, where he attended
high school and medical school; he later received his DPhil from
Oxford University, UK. One of the pioneers of modern molecular
biology, Brenner was instrumental in deciphering the basic principles
of the genetic code. In the 1960s, together with Francis Crick,
Brenner showed that the code is composed of non-overlapping
triplets; in collaboration with François Jacob and Matthew Meselson,
he went on to demonstrate the existence of messenger RNA.

Brenner is also known for spearheading the use of the nematode
worm *Caenorhabditis elegans* as a model organism for understanding
human biology. He was later awarded the 2002 Nobel Prize in
Physiology or Medicine (with H. Robert Horvitz and John E. Sulston)
for his work in *C. elegans* on the genetics of programmed cell death.
In the genomic era, Brenner developed new methods for next-
generation DNA sequencing, and initiated a project to sequence
the compact genome of the Japanese pufferfish or *fugu*.

Brenner is currently scientific advisor to the chairman at the Agency
for Science, Technology and Research (A*STAR), Singapore, and
an adjunct professor at the Lee Kong Chian School of Medicine,
Nanyang Technology University, Singapore, among other affiliations.
He continues to work on genomes and their evolution

ACKNOWLEDGEMENTS

The editors would first and foremost like to thank Sydney Brenner for conceiving *10-on-10: The Chronicles of Evolution*, the lecture series upon which this book is based. We are grateful for his guidance throughout the book's production, and for his contribution of the foreword and epilogue.

The *10-on-10* lecture series was organised by the Para Limes Society of Nanyang Technological University (NTU), Singapore, and the Agency for Science, Technology and Research (A*STAR), Singapore.

We thank Jan W. Vasbinder and Balázs Gulyás of Para Limes, as well as Asyifah Rashid of A*STAR, for designing the series, identifying its distinguished speakers and organising the lectures.

Special thanks to Karen Chung, who as head of the *10-on-10* secretariat was the series' de facto organiser. She made each session an engaging, enjoyable experience for speakers and audience members alike.

We are grateful for the support of a team of excellent advisors, some of whom also acted as session moderators and panellists. In particular, we would like to thank Barry Halliwell, David Lane, Daniela Rhodes, Michael Khor and Christoph Winkler.

The *10-on-10* lecture series and this book also received strong backing from senior leadership at A*STAR and NTU; we are grateful to Lim Chuan Poh, Bertil Andersson and Subra Suresh for their support.

Without appropriate lecture venues, the *10-on-10* lecture series would not have been the same. We thank the ArtScience Museum, the Biopolis, the Lee Kong Chian School of Medicine at NTU, the National Library Board and the S.E.A. Aquarium at Resorts World Sentosa for generously opening up their facilities.

At the successful conclusion of the lecture series, the talented editorial and design teams at Wildtype Media Group took over to craft and produce this book. Jeremy Chan, Rebecca Tan and Juliana Chan condensed hours of complex material into engaging, readable chapters; Oi Keat Lam, with help from Allan Chan, designed and laid out each and every page of the book.

The book's jacket was illustrated by Kelsey Oseid; contributor portraits were illustrated by Lianne Chua.

Our special appreciation to UBS AG for its generous support and kind donation of the books to libraries and schools across Southeast Asia.

*This book was made possible with the support of A*STAR.*

Agency for
Science, Technology
and Research

SINGAPORE

INDEX

IMAGE CREDITS

WILDTYPE BOOKS

Sydney Brenner's 10-on-10: The Chronicles of Evolution
Copyright © 2019 Agency for Science, Technology and Research

ISBN: 978-981-11-8718-6 (hardcover)
ISBN: 978-981-11-8831-2 (softcover)

Published in Singapore by Wildtype Books, an imprint of
Wildtype Media Group, Singapore

www.wildtype.media

Printed in Singapore

First published under this imprint in 2019

Cataloguing-in-publication data for this book is available from
the National Library Board, Singapore